Electrons and the Nucleus

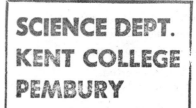

John Murray
in association with
Inner London Education Authority

APPIL First Edition Project Team
John Bausor (Director)
Leslie Beckett
Allan Covell
David Davies
Martin Hollins

APPIL Revised Edition
Co-ordinated by Martin Hollins
This unit has been revised by Martin Hollins and edited by Allan Covell

Design, typesetting and page layout by Tony Langham
Diagrams by Technical Art Services and John Sangwin

© 1989 Inner London Education Authority

Published by John Murray (Publishers) Ltd,
50 Albemarle Street, London W1X 4BD

APPIL first edition 1979–80
This edition 1989

Reprinted 1991, 1995

Printed in Great Britain by St Edmundsbury Press Ltd

British Library Cataloguing in Publication Data

Electrons and the nucleus.
  I. ILEA Physics Project Team II. Advanced Physics
  Project for Independent Learning
  539.7'2112
  ISBN 0–7195–4580–3

Contents

How to use APPIL

APPIL is a programme for independent learning. This unit is not a textbook: it is a guide to using texts, experiments and other resources to help you to learn about the topics in your A-level physics syllabus.

There are sections of text in this unit which are to be read as in any other book, but much of the guide is concerned with helping you through other activities designed to produce effective learning when you work independently. For a fuller explanation of the way APPIL is written you should read the *Student's resource book*. What follows is a brief summary.

Objectives

What is to be learnt is stated at the beginning of each topic - a general statement of what you will be doing, and more detailed objectives to be achieved. The objectives are particularly important, because they tell you what you should be able to do when you have finished working through the topic, and so give you extra help in organising your learning. You will probably wish to refer to them when you have finished each topic.

Experiments

E Experiment FM 12
Barton's pendulums

The aim of this experiment is to observe what happens when a system is made to vibrate at some frequency other than its own natural frequency of vibration.

These are a very important part of the course. Each experiment is referred to at the most appropriate time in the text. You should aim to organise your work so that it can be done at that time. Most experiments should not take longer than an hour if the apparatus is available. The experiments are listed at the beginning of each topic, with an estimate of the time required and notes of any other factors to be taken account of in planning. Each experiment contains questions which require written answers. In general, there is no value in copying out the instructions given, but notes on any details which might be useful for revision should be made.

Self-assessment questions

Q 5.19 Self-assessment question

A hi-fi record-player turntable has a mass of 1.28 kg and a radius of gyration about its centre of 25 cm. What is its moment of inertia? What torque will be required to accelerate it up to 33 r.p.m. in 1 second? ■

These test your understanding of the work you have done, and will help you to check your progress. They are not intended to be difficult: you should be able to answer most of them quite easily.

The answers to self-assessment questions are given at the end of the book, but if you look at the answer before you have tried the question you will not be involved in the learning process and your learning may suffer.

■ indicates the end of a question.

Development questions

These are included to involve you in a proof or idea which is being developed in the text. The answer to a development question is usually in the text, but involving yourself in the development helps you to learn: just looking at the answer is not so effective. If the answer is given at the end of the book the question is marked with an asterisk*.

Discussion questions

Q 5.33 Discussion question

Some small toy cars use for propulsion the energy stored in a flywheel; these toys are popularly known as 'friction-powered'. Why? What would be a better name?

How does a yo-yo work?

Can you find any other examples of toys using 'rotatory stores' of energy? How about designing one? ■

These are questions where there is no 'right answer'. Often they cover technical applications, problem-solving and social issues. It is suggested that you do some background research and reading - or just thinking, to answer these.

Study questions

For these you will need to use resources apart from this unit: for example, textbooks or experimental results. For all questions, general references are given to basic books at the start of each topic. It is not expected that you will be able to consult all the references given but you should always use more than one when possible.

This type of question usually requires longer answers than the others. These answers, in many cases, form a basis for your notes for the final examination and are therefore very important. Full answers are not usually given in this guide, though hints and partial answers are sometimes given. These questions are marked with an asterisk. Your answers to study questions should be handed in regularly for marking.

Questions on objectives

> 1 A particle moves with a uniform angular velocity ω in a circular path of radius r. Show that the projection of the motion of the particle on a diameter of the circle is simple harmonic motion. *(objective 4)*

These are groups of questions which come at the end of each topic and are related to the objectives at the beginning of each topic. Answering these will help you to tell whether you have achieved the objectives. The answers are given in the *Student's resource book*.

End-of-unit test

This is to enable your teacher to check the value of the course to you. You will be asked to do this test when you have completed the unit, and will be given details at the appropriate time.

Examination questions

Questions in the test, and some of the other questions, are taken from past papers. Your teacher will probably set some more of these during the course, for revision purposes.

Audio-visual aids /Computer programs

> **C** Computer program
> **Simple harmonic motion**
>
> This program enables you to explore simple harmonic motion and its relationship with uniform circular motion.

Audio-visual aids and computer programs are recommended in some topics. You should ask your teacher if these are available.

Background reading

> Background reading
>
> For an exciting account of the work of Galileo and Newton, read Koestler, A. *The sleepwalkers*.

This refers to books which are useful for a more detailed study of certain topics. They are also often interesting to read in their own right, and sometimes put the physics of the syllabus in its historical, social or technological context.

References

References are made where appropriate to textbooks. A list of the abbreviations used can be found at the end of this unit.

Comprehension

> **C** Comprehension FM 2
> **Building the wind-up tube train**
>
> This is an article on the use of flywheels in the New York underground system.

These extracts from recent scientific and technological articles have a similar aim. They are followed by questions designed to check your understanding. They will be found in Part 4 of the *Student's resource book*.

Extension

> **EXTENSION**
>
> **Q** 2.30 Study question
>
> (a) Why is a violin box shaped the way it is? (b) How can a violinist change the quality of note produced by this instrument? (c) In what other shapes are sound boxes made? Suggest how they affect the sound produced.■

These boxed sections are included to provide:

(a) additional material of general interest and importance, or
(b) more detailed treatment of topics for more able students.

Sections marked ● are not required for some syllabuses and may provide additional useful extension material. Your teacher will advise you of the particular requirements of your syllabus.

Organising your time

In this programme of work there is a variety of activities. Some of them, like experiments, need a laboratory, and you may also need to use the library. You must, therefore, organise your time so that you can make the best use of the resources available.

When you start a topic, look through it and see what activities are included, then allocate each activity a time on your work schedule. Make sure, for example, that you do the experiments when you are timetabled in a laboratory. Follow the sequence in this guide if you can, but this may not always be possible.

The recommended time for completion of the work in each topic is given at the beginning of each topic. This assumes that you spend 8-10 hours each week on physics, divided between class time, private study and home study. It is important to try to complete the unit in a set time. You should ask your teacher for a **progress monitor**. It will help you to plan your time.

APPIL EN

Introduction to the Unit

This unit is a study of electrons and the nuclear atom. It traces the development of the understanding of the nature of matter and its implications in the diverse fields of electronics, radioactivity and nuclear physics. Many topics are developed chronologically with accounts of the important discoveries of the three decades at the start of this century. The interplay of key experiment and critical theory is shown as this builds up a picture of the fundamental nature of matter-energy.

Topic 1 starts with the nature of electrons, how they were discovered and how their charge can be measured.

In **topic 2** you will study the nature and properties of ionising radiations. This knowledge is used in topic 3 in studying Rutherford's model of the nuclear atom.

The behaviour of radioactive substances and their uses is the subject of **topic 4** which includes a review of the potential hazards of radiation.

A range of important nuclear reactions is covered in **topic 5**, with a more detailed look at fission and fusion as sources of power.

Topic 6 introduces the photoelectric effect and its explanation by Einstein using the quantum theory.

The wave-particle duality of matter-energy is applied to electrons in **topic 7** which presents a contemporary model of the atom.

Recommended study times

You should spend 8-10 weeks on this unit as follows;-

Topic 1	1 weeks
Topic 2	1.5-2 weeks
Topic 3	1.5 weeks
Topic 4	1.5 weeks
Topic 5	1.5 weeks
Topic 6	1 week
Topic 7	1 week

Free electrons

Summary

In this topic you will learn how electron streams can be produced, and about their properties. You will study the experimental evidence which led to the discovery of the electron, the measurement of its specific charge and the determination of the fundamental unit of charge - the magnitude of the charge on one electron.

What other knowledge is required to design a television picture tube?

Objectives

When you have completed the work in this topic you should be able to:

1 Use correctly the following scientific terms: specific charge, thermionic valve.

2 Explain what is meant by the thermionic effect and describe an experiment to demonstrate the effect.

3 Explain what is meant by the work function of a metal and state its unit.

4 List the principal properties of cathode rays (electron streams).

5 Describe an experiment to determine the specific charge of electrons and show how the result is derived from the observations.

6 Describe an experiment to determine the charge of the electron, show how the value is derived from the observations and comment on the significance of the results.

7 Solve problems involving the deflection of electrons in electric and magnetic fields, the specific charge and the charge on the electron.

Experiments

EN 1 The specific charge of the electron   (1 - 1.5 hours)

References

Akrill	Chapters 15 and 18
Caro	Chapter 2
Duncan	Chapter 20
Muncaster	Chapter 50
Nelkon	Chapter 31
Wenham	Chapters 31 and 33
Whelan	Chapter 60

1.1 Introduction

The discovery of electrons arose from the study of conduction of electricity through gases at low pressure. When a current was passed through gas in a discharge tube, scientists had observed fluorescence in the walls of the tube opposite the cathode. It was clear that something was travelling down the tube from the cathode so the name 'cathode rays' was used. Were the cathode rays a form of electromagnetic radiation, like light, or some type of particle? This question was a matter of controversy in scientific circles for several years. In 1897, J.J. Thomson published the results of his experimental work which firmly established that the rays were fast-moving negative particles - electrons.

Support for Thomson's work came from other sources. Negative particles are emitted from metals heated to a high temperature (the thermionic effect), and when electromagnetic radiation of less than a certain wavelength is incident on a metallic surface (the photoelectric effect). In all cases the value of the specific charge (the rate of charge to mass) for these negative particles, produced in different ways, was the same so they were recognised as identical. We will start by looking at these emissions and their behaviour before reviewing Thomson's measurement of the specific charge in section 1.4.

1.2 Thermionic emission

When a piece of metal is heated to a high temperature, it is found that electrons are emitted from its surface. This is known as the **thermionic effect**. The free electrons or conduction electrons in the metal may acquire an increase in their kinetic energy which is sufficient to enable them to escape from the surface of the metal; this is similar to the escape of molecules from the surface of a liquid.

Evidence for thermionic electrons

To establish the idea that when a metal filament is heated negative charges (i.e. electrons) are released, we can consider the results of the following experiment.

Q 1.1 Development question*

The evacuated tube shown in figure 1.1 contains a heated filament and a metal plate (called the anode). The results in table 1.1 were obtained when the potential difference across the tube was varied.

Table 1.1

p.d. V_{AC}/V	current I_A/mA	p.d. V_{AC}/V	current I_A/mA
-200	0.0	200	2.2
-100	0.0	250	2.5
- 50	0.0	300	2.6
0	0.0	350	2.7
50	0.2	400	2.8
100	0.6	450	2.8
150	1.6	500	2.8

(a) Plot a graph of the current (y-axis) against the corresponding potential difference (x-axis).
(b) What does your graph tell you about the conducting property of such a device?
(c) Explain why the results show that *both* positive and negative charges cannot be available from the filament. ∎

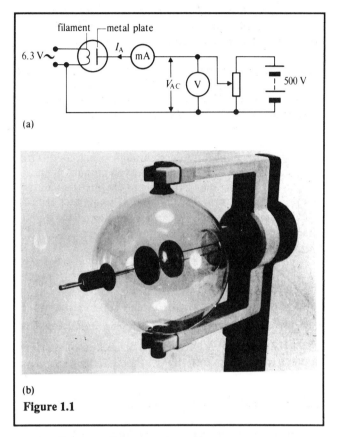

(a)

(b)
Figure 1.1

An electric current passes only when the plate is positive. The current through the tube is due to negative charge that is being given off by the hot filament. Note that the current can flow only one way. If the potential is reversed the flow shuts off, since the anode is not heated.

This is an example of a **thermionic valve**. The simplest of these has two electrodes, like the device used in the experiment, and is called a **diode**. The flow of electrons can, however, be usefully controlled by the addition of further electrodes, as in a triode with three. A wide range of valves was developed in the earlier part of this century for use such as amplification in radio communications. They made possible the first electronics industry. They have several disadvantages, however. They are similar in size to light bulbs and rather more fragile, and because they operate on the heating effect, they require considerable power. Semiconducting devices have now superseded them in most applications. These are covered in the unit *Behaviour of matter*.

Work function of a metal

Q 1.2 Study question

(a) In the free electron theory of metallic bonding, to what extent are the electrons free? What is fixed?
(b) What prevents electrons leaving the metal at ordinary

temperatures? If an electron did leave the surface, what could you say about its energy?

(c) Describe very briefly the three ways, called thermionic emission, photoelectric emission and field emission, in which electrons can be removed from the metal.
What is the source of energy in each case? ∎

Note: The modern solid-state theory considers the different energy levels which an electron can occupy within the solid; however, at this stage a simplified view is adequate.

Energy is required to remove an electron from the surface of a metal. The energy that must be supplied to enable an electron to escape from the surface of a metal is called the **work function** Φ . It is sometimes measured in electron volts, eV.

Note. The potential difference through which an electron must be accelerated if it is to acquire an amount of energy equal to Φ is sometimes referred to as the work function and to add to the confusion the symbol *W* is sometimes used for the work function.

Q 1.3 Self-assessment question

(a) Calculate the kinetic energy in joules acquired by an electron when it is accelerated through a p.d. of 1 V.
(b) The work function of sodium is 2.5 eV. Calculate the energy in joules which is required to release an electron from the surface of the metal.
(Charge on electron = -1.6×10^{-19} C) ∎

1.3 Properties of electron streams

Electrons which are travelling at high speed are called cathode rays. Although we could find out about the properties of cathode rays using a cold cathode tube (historically this is how they were discovered) it is safer and more convenient to use electrons that are produced by a heated filament. The properties can be demonstrated using specially designed tubes and these experiments may be shown to you by your teacher.

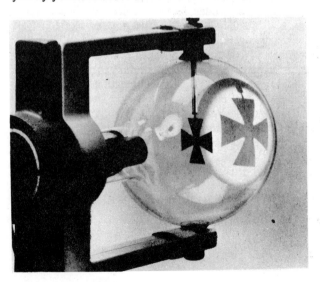

Figure 1.2

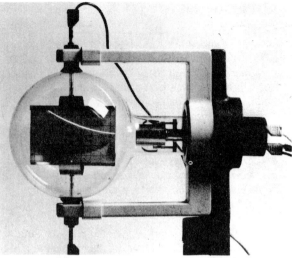

Figure 1.3

In the tube shown in figure 1.2, electrons pass through a hole in the anode to form a divergent beam. An object (in the form of a Maltese cross) casts a shadow on the fluorescent screen. Thus, the electron stream *travels in straight lines*.

When a p.d. is applied between two horizontal plates, as in figure 1.3, the electron beam is deflected towards the positive plate. Electrons may be *deflected* by an *electric field*.

Figure 1.4

The electron beam may also be passed through a magnetic field produced by a magnet or by a current passing through two suitably placed coils, figure 1.4. The electron beam is deflected into a circular path. Electrons may be *deflected* by a *magnetic field*.

Q 1.4 Self-assessment question

How do these observations suggest that the charge on the electron is negative? ∎

Confirmation of the fact that electrons have a negative charge can be obtained using the tube shown in figure 1.5. The electron beam can be deflected by a magnetic field into a metal cylinder.

The cylinder is connected to a leaf electroscope which has been negatively charged. When the electrons are deflected into the cylinder the leaf rises further.

Figure 1.5

Q 1.5 Study question

Write a brief summary of the properties of electron streams. ∎

One of the important properties of electrons is that they are deflected by electric and magnetic fields. The ability to control the movement of electrons has led to the development of instruments such as the cathode ray tube and electron microscope, and to technical applications such as electron beam welding.

In the unit *Forces and fields*, you derived expressions for the forces which are exerted on charged particles by electric and magnetic fields and found out about their subsequent motion in these fields. These expressions are summarised in the following sub-sections.

Speed of electrons

If the p.d. between the anode and cathode of an electron gun is V, then the kinetic energy W acquired by an electron is given by

$$W = eV$$

But $$W = \tfrac{1}{2}mv^2$$

Therefore $$eV = \tfrac{1}{2}mv^2$$

This is an important equation which enables the speed of the electron to be calculated.

Deflection of an electron in a magnetic field

The force F_B which is exerted on an electron travelling with a speed v at right angles to a uniform magnetic field of flux density B is given by

$$F_B = Bev$$

The force F_B is perpendicular to the plane of B and v.

The path taken by the electron is a circular arc and the equation which describes the motion is given by

$$\frac{mv^2}{r} = B\,e\,v$$

Deflection of an electron in an electric field

The force F_E which is exerted on an electron which enters an electric field of electric field strength E at right angles to the original direction of motion is given by

$$F_E = E\,e$$

The force F_E is parallel to E but oppositely directed.

The path taken by the electron is a **parabola.**

Q 1.6 Self-assessment question

Electrons in a cathode ray tube are accelerated through a p.d. of 3.0 kV between the cathode and screen. Calculate the speed with which they strike the screen.

(Charge on electron = -1.6 x 10^{-19} C,
mass of electron = 9.1 x 10^{-31} kg) ∎

Q 1.7 Self-assessment question

Calculate the least magnetic flux density of a magnetic field which would be required to make an electron travelling with a speed 8.0 x 10^6 m s^{-1}, travel in a circular path of diameter 15 cm. ∎

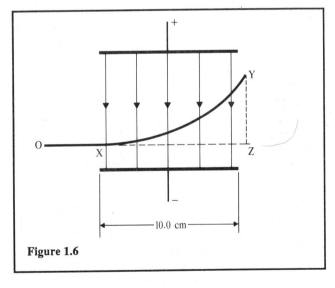

Figure 1.6

Q 1.8 Self-assessment question

A beam of electrons travelling at 4.0 x 10^7 m s^{-1} in a vacuum enters an electric field at X and leaves it at Y (figure 1.6). The initial direction of motion is along OX, perpendicular to the electric field. The electric field of intensity 1.0 x 10^5 V m^{-1} can be assumed to be uniform in the region between the plates and zero everywhere else.

(a) Why is the horizontal component of the electrons' velocity unchanged by the action of the electric field?

(b) If the length of the plates is 10 cm, calculate the time that the electrons spend in the electric field.

(c) Calculate the force exerted on the electrons while they are in the electric field.

(d) Calculate the acceleration of the electrons in the vertical direction.

(e) Calculate the vertical displacement ZY.

(f) In what direction do the electrons travel after leaving the field at Y? ■

1.4 Measurement of specific charge of electrons

J.J. Thomson's experiments on the deflection of cathode rays in 'crossed' electric and magnetic fields enabled him to calculate the speed of cathode rays and hence deduce a value for e/m_e (the specific charge) where e is the charge and m_e the mass of each cathode ray particle.

He found that the speed was about 10^7 m s^{-1} (thus providing evidence that they were not a form of electromagnetic waves like light). He also found that the specific charge did not depend upon the nature of the gas in the discharge tube (evidence that cathode rays do not consist of charged atoms, otherwise the specific charge would depend upon the nature of the gas). His value of e/m_e was over a thousand times greater than that for hydrogen ions. Should this large value of e/m_e be interpreted as a large value of the charge e or a small value of the mass m_e? The penetrating power of cathode rays (investigated by Lenard) implied a small charge, hence they were lighter than atoms.

Thomson's views on the nature of cathode rays were as follows:

'The explanation which seems to me to account in the most simple and straightforward manner for the facts is ... that the atoms of the different chemical elements are different aggregations of atoms of the same kind. If, in the very intense electric field in the neighbourhood of the cathode, the molecules of the gas are dissociated and are split up, not into the ordinary chemical atoms, but into these primordial atoms which we shall for brevity call corpuscles; and if these corpuscles are charged with electricity and projected from the cathode by the electric field, they would behave exactly like cathode rays.'

Thus on this view we have, in cathode rays, matter in a new state in which the subdivision of matter is carried very much further than in the ordinary gaseous state; a state which all matter - that is, matter derived from different sources such as hydrogen, oxygen, etc. - is of one and the same kind; this matter being the substance from which all the chemical elements are built up.'

He concluded

'that atoms are not indivisible for negatively electrified particles (electrons) can be torn from them by the action of electrical forces.'

This picture of atoms losing electrons was revolutionary because it involved the new idea that the electron is an essential part of a neutral atom.

We will consider two methods for the measurement of e/m_e. The determination of e/m_e is important because it enables us to calculate the mass of the electron providing the value of the charge e is known. It is not possible to determine experimentally the mass of the electron.

Electron tube using crossed fields

The principle of this method is similar to that developed by J.J. Thomson. A beam of electrons passes through two fields, an electric field and a magnetic field arranged so that the beam is undeflected when it emerges from the combined field (figure 1.7).

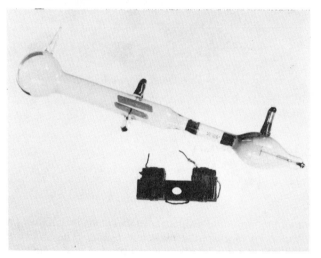

Figure 1.7

The illustration shows the tube and the magnetic deflection coils devised and used by J.J. Thomson in his experiments to determine the ratio of e/m_e for 'cathode rays' (electrons).

Q 1.9 Development question*

A beam of electrons which is travelling into the plane of the diagram (figure 1.8) is accelerated in an electron gun through a p.d. of V. It then passes between two parallel deflecting plates which produce an electric field perpendicular to the original direction of the beam.

(a) Copy the diagram (figure 1.8) and mark on it the direction of the electric field E and the force F_E which is exerted on an electron by the electric field.

A magnetic field, produced by two circular coils, is superimposed on the electric field and acts over the same region. The magnetic flux density of the field is such that the beam of electrons passes through the two fields undeviated from its original direction.

(b) Show on your diagram the position of the two circular coils and mark the direction of the force F_B which is exerted on the electron by the magnetic field and the magnetic flux density B.

(c) Show that the speed of the electron beam is given by the expression

$$v = E/B$$

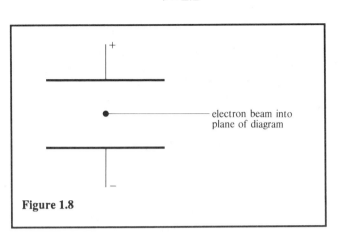

electron beam into plane of diagram

Figure 1.8

(d) The kinetic energy of the electrons is given by equation

$$\tfrac{1}{2}m_\mathrm{e}v^2 = eV$$

where V is the p.d. between the filament and anode.

If the p.d. across the parallel plates that produces the electric field is equal to V between the filament and anode, show that

$$\frac{e}{m_\mathrm{e}} = \frac{V}{2B^2d^2}$$

where d is the distance between the plates.

(e) What measurements will enable e/m_e to be calculated? ∎

Fine beam tube method

A fine beam tube is a special type of electron gun tube which contains a gas at low pressure. This makes the path of the electron beam visible.

Figure 1.9

A magnetic field is arranged in such a way that the beam of electrons moves in a circular orbit, as illustrated in figure 1.9.

Q 1.10 Development question*

Electrons which were emitted from the filament of an electron gun are accelerated through a p.d. of V, then enter a uniform magnetic field of magnetic flux density B and travel in a circular path of radius r.

(a) State clearly the direction of the force F_B which is exerted on the electrons and the direction of the magnetic field.
(b) Justify the expression

$$Bev = \frac{m\,v^2}{r}$$

and hence show that

$$\frac{e}{m_\mathrm{e}} = \frac{2V}{B^2\,r^2}$$

(c) What measurements will enable e/m_e to be calculated?∎

Note. The derivation of this equation is important; it is the basic equation for the motion of charged particles in a uniform magnetic field. You will meet it again when you consider the cyclotron, which is a machine designed to accelerate particles to high energy (i.e. very high speed).

You should now do either experiment EN 1 or study question 1.11. There is no need to do both, for obvious reasons, but you should do the experiment, if possible.

E Experiment EN 1
The specific charge of the electron

The aim of this experiment is to measure the specific charge e/m_e of the electron by a deflection tube method.

Q 1.11 Study question

Describe an experiment which will enable you to determine the specific charge of the electron. You should include in your account details of the design of the apparatus, the experimental procedure, the observations that you would make and the limits of the accuracy of the experiment. ∎

Q 1.12 Self-assessment question

(a) An electron emitted from a heated filament in an evacuated tube is accelerated through a p.d. of 4000 V and then enters at right angles a uniform magnetic field of magnetic flux density 1.0×10^{-3} tesla. Calculate the speed of the electron and the radius of its path in the magnetic field.
(e/m_e for electron = -1.8×10^{11} C kg^{-1})
(b) Calculate the strength of a uniform electric field which, when suitably applied, would cause the electron to travel in a straight line from the filament.
(c) Show on a diagram the direction of the motion of the electron relative to the directions of the electric and magnetic fields. ∎

This account of J.J. Thomson's work by his son George, stresses the importance of a hypothesis in experimental physics.

1.5 The charge of the electron

Evidence for the fact that electric charge, like matter, exists only in discrete amounts (i.e. there is a basic unit of electric charge) was put forward in the nineteenth century by Michael Faraday as a result of his work on electrolysis.

Q 1.13 Study question*

(a) What is meant by the Faraday constant F?
(b) What is meant by the Avogadro constant N_A?
(c) Write down an equation relating F, N_A and e (where e is the charge carried by a singly charged ion). ∎

Millikan's oil drop experiment

In 1910, R.A. Millikan published the results of a series of experiments that he had carried out over many years which supplied evidence for the particulate nature of electricity, i.e. it consists of a fundamental packet of electric charge, not a continuous fluid, and he obtained a value for this basic unit of charge (which is the charge of the electron). The principle of his method was to observe the motion of charged oil drops in an electric field. A schematic diagram of the apparatus used is shown in figure 1.10. He found that the charges on the oil drops were always a multiple of the lowest charge e, i.e. $+e$, $+2e$, $+3e$, $+...$ He never found fractional multiples of e. This was the first experiment to show that electric charge (or, if you prefer it, electricity) has a particle nature just as matter has.

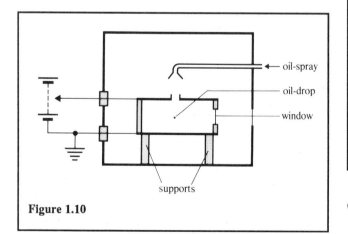

Figure 1.10

Q 1.14 Development question*

(a) In the first part of the experiment the drop was allowed to fall freely under gravity.
(i) What two forces act on the oil drop? (Neglect the hydrostatic upthrust of the air on the drop.)

(ii) When the oil drop, radius r, has acquired a steady speed v_1, what do you know about the two forces?
(iii) Justify the expression

$$mg = krv_1$$

Note. For a very slow motion of a sphere through a viscous fluid the flow of the medium round the sphere is streamlined and the drag force of fluid friction is given by $F = krv$ where k is a constant which depends upon the nature of the fluid. (This was considered in the unit *Behaviour of matter*.)

(iv) Show that the radius of the drop is given by

$$r^2 = \frac{3kv_1}{4\pi\rho g}$$

where ρ is the density of the oil. (Strictly, this should be the difference in density between oil and air. Why?)

From this part of the experiment the radius of the drop, and hence the mass, can be determined.

(b) In the second part of the experiment a potential difference was applied across the plates and adjusted until a charged oil drop remained stationary.
(i) Copy the diagram (figure 1.11a) and show the forces acting on the oil drop.

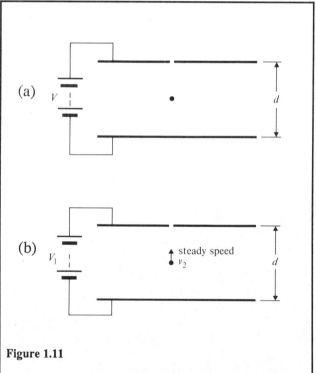

Figure 1.11

(ii) Justify the following expression

$$mg = \frac{VQ}{d}$$

where Q is the charge on the oil drop and V is the potential difference between the plates.

From this equation, the charge on the oil drop can be calculated.

(c) In practice, it is difficult to adjust the value of the electric field so that the drop remains stationary and a more accurate result can be obtained by adjusting the field so that the oil drop rises with uniform velocity between the plates.

(i) Suppose that the potential difference between the plates is V_1 and that the drop moves upwards with a steady speed v_2.

Copy the diagram (figure 1.11b) and show the forces acting on the oil drop.

(ii) Justify the expression

$$\frac{V_1 Q}{d} = mg\left(1 + \frac{v_2}{v_1}\right)$$

Since m has been deduced from the first series of observations the magnitude of Q can be calculated. ■

From observation on a large number of droplets, Millikan obtained different values for the charge carried by each of them.

The important result was that he did not observe a single charge smaller than 1.591×10^{-19} C and that all the other charges were integral multiples of this value. Thus, he demonstrated the particulate nature of electricity and, at the same time, determined the value of the fundamental unit of charge, i.e. the charge of the electron. The currently accepted value of the elementary charge is
$e = -1.6021 \times 10^{-19}$ C.

The mass of the electron is determined by combining the accurate measurements of e and e/m_e.

Q 1.15 Study question

Give an account of a method by which the fundamental unit of charge (i.e. the charge of the electron) has been measured. You should include a diagram of the apparatus, and details of the experimental procedure. ■

Q 1.16 Self-assessment question

(a) Millikan found that the terminal velocity of an oil drop remained constant for many hours. However, with a water droplet the speed decreased. Account for this and state what you can deduce about the oil.

(b) When an electric field was applied between the plates, Millikan observed that the oil drop moved up with a uniform velocity which remained steady for several trips.

On occasions, he observed a sudden change to a new velocity which appeared to happen more frequently after an X-ray tube was switched on nearby. How do you account for this fact? ■

Q 1.17 Self-assessment question

The results shown in table 1.2 were obtained with a Millikan apparatus, using oil drops. The distance between the plates was 4.42 mm.

Table 1.2

p.d. to balance drop/V	weight of drop/x 10^{-14} N
470	5.05
820	5.90
230	3.35
770	2.85
1030	3.65
395	7.00

(a) Find the size of the charge on each drop.
(b) Identify a basic charge e such that each charge Q is some whole number N of e. ■

Q 1.18 Self-assessment question

An oil drop in air between two horizontal metal plates falls with a uniform velocity of 0.4 mm s^{-1} when both plates are earthed (i.e. no electric field between the plates). When a p.d. of 6900 V is maintained between the plates, separated by a distance of 1.3×10^{-2} m, the drop remains at rest. If the resistance to motion is given by the equation $F = k r v$, where r is the radius of the drop, v is the speed and k is a constant, calculate (a) the radius of the drop and (b) the charge on the oil drop.
[Density of oil $= 0.9 \times 10^3$ kg m^{-3} $k = 6 \pi \times 1.8 \times 10^{-5}$ Pa s (N s m^{-2})] ■

C Computer program
MILLIKAN Millikan oil drop experiment

This program simulates the experiment in which the potential difference between the plates is varied so that a charged drop is held stationary between the plates. The charge on the drops can be shown to be an integral multiple of the basic unit of charge.

EXPERIMENT EN 1

The specific charge of the electron

Apparatus

○ deflection tube
○ pair of coils
○ stand for tube
○ e.h.t. power supply

○ ammeter 4, 0-1 A
○ variable resistor, 10-15 Ω 12 V battery or smooth d.c. supply, 0-25 V
○ 6.3 V heater supply

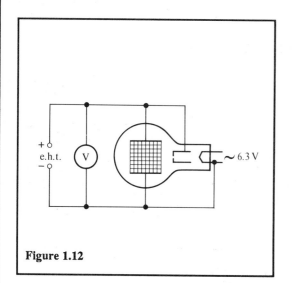

Figure 1.12

Obtaining a circular track

1 Connect up the circuit as shown in figure 1.12.

Note. Before switching on any supplies, adjust the variable control of the e.h.t. supply so that the output p.d. will be zero. Switch on the 6.3 V supply and then slowly increase the anode to cathode potential difference until a blue line appears on the screen. (It should become visible at a p.d. of about 2000 V.)

2 Adjust the p.d. to about 2500 V and record the reading on the voltmeter on the e.h.t. unit.

3 Connect up the current supply to the coils as in figure 1.13 and adjust the variable resistance so that part of a circular path is obtained on the screen.

Note. If you do not obtain a circular path as the current is increased, then it is likely that the coils are incorrectly connected - the connections to one of them should be reversed.

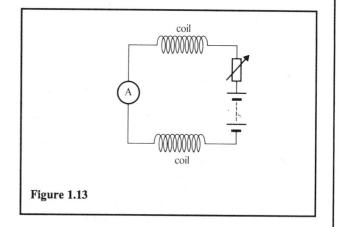

Figure 1.13

4 Record the reading on the ammeter of the current *I* through the coils.

continued

EXPERIMENT EN1

Measurement of the radius of the track

The coordinates of three points A, B and C on the circular path should be noted, one near the beginning, one near the end and one in between. Transfer these points to graph paper and use the construction method as shown in figure 1.14 to determine the centre of the circular path. Measure the radius r.

Measurement of the magnetic flux density

The magnetic flux density B can be measured experimentally by a current balances (for details see the unit *Forces and fields*, or calculated from the expression for the field due to the Helmholtz coils. It is given by

$$B = \frac{8\mu_0 NI}{5\sqrt{5}r}$$

where N is the number of turns and r is the radius of the coil.

Calculation of e/m_e

The energy of the electrons is controlled by the potential difference V across the electron gun and is given by the relationship

$$\tfrac{1}{2}m_e v^2 = eV$$

The force F_B exerted on the electrons in the magnetic field is

$$F_B = Bev = \frac{m_e v^2}{r}$$

From the two equations it can be shown that

$$\frac{e}{m_e} = \frac{2V}{B^2 r^2}$$

Use your results to calculate a value for e/m_e.

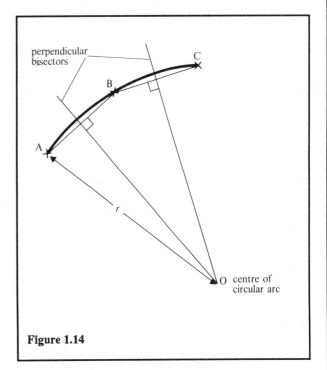

Figure 1.14

Questions on objectives

1 Describe an experiment to demonstrate thermionic emission of electrons. *(objective 2)*

2 Explain what is meant by the work function of a metal. *(objective 3)*

3 Give a summary of the chief properties of electron streams (cathode rays). *(objective 4)*

4 A charged oil drop of weight 2.4×10^{-14} N has a charge of 6.4×10^{-19} C. It is held stationary between two horizontal plates which are 20 mm apart by applying a p.d. to the plates. Calculate the p.d. that would be required. Explain your reasoning. *(objective 7)*

5 Electrons in an evacuated tube are accelerated from rest through a p.d. of 3.6 kV and then travel in a narrow beam before entering a uniform magnetic field which is perpendicular to the beam. In the magnetic field, the electrons travel in a circular arc of radius 0.10 m. Calculate

(a) the speed of the electrons entering the magnetic field,
(b) the magnetic flux density of the magnetic field.
($e/m_e = 1.8 \times 10^{11}$ C kg^{-1}) *(objective 7)*

6 (a) Write down expressions for the force on a moving electric charge in an electric field, and in a magnetic field. State the meanings of the symbols and indicate clearly the direction of the force in each case.
(b) Describe an experiment utilising one or both of these expressions which enables the ratio e/m_e for electrons to be determined. Derive an expression for e/m_e in terms of measurable quantities and state clearly how these quantities would be determined.
(c) Electrons are accelerated from rest by a potential difference of 100 V and are then collimated in a field-free region to form a fine pencil beam as shown in figure 1.15. They then enter the shaded region where a uniform magnetic field exists which is perpendicular to the plane of the diagram.

Assuming for purposes of calculation that the field is uniform over the shaded region and is zero elsewhere, calculate the flux density of the field required to deflect the electrons through 90° so as to emerge as shown.
($e/m_e = -1.76 \times 10^{11}$ C kg^{-1}) *(objectives 5 and 7)*

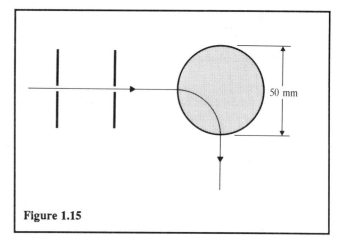

Figure 1.15

7 (a) Giving all relevant equations, describe how the electron charge may be found from observations of the motion of a charged oil drop moving vertically in a vertical electric field.
(b) An oil drop of mass 2.0×10^{-15} kg falls at its terminal velocity between a pair of *vertical* parallel plates. When a potential gradient of 5.0×10^4 V m^{-1} is maintained between the plates, the direction of fall becomes inclined at an angle of 21° 48' to the vertical. Draw vector diagrams to illustrate the forces acting on the drop (a) before, and (b) after, the field is applied. Give formulae for the magnitude of the vectors involved. (Stokes' law may be assumed and the Archimedes' upthrust ignored.)

Calculate the charge on the drop.
($g = 10$ m s^{-2}) *(objectives 6 and 7)*

Summary

In this topic you will study the properties and nature of the three types of ionising radiation. This will involve doing experiments using different detectors and sources. One such detector, the cloud chamber, displays tracks for each radiation of the type shown here. Can you tell which is which?

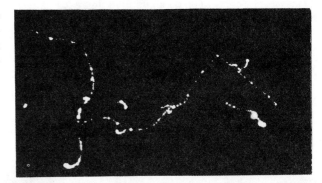

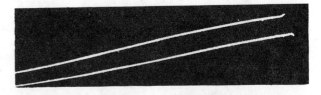

Objectives

When you have completed the work in this chapter you should be able to:

1 Use the following scientific terms correctly: ionising radiation, radioactive, ionisation current, background radiation.

2 Describe how to detect radiation photographically.

3 Explain the structure of the following instruments and use them to detect and measure ionising radiation: ionising chamber, cloud chamber, Geiger-Müller tube.

4 Perform and describe experiments to show the following properties of ionising radiations: ionisation, penetration, deflection in magnetic fields.

5 Recall the natures of alpha, beta and gamma radiations and relate these to their chief properties.

6 Recall the types of biological damage resulting from radiations.

7 Recall, explain and follow laboratory procedures designed to reduce exposure to radiation to an acceptable level.

Experiments

EN 2 Photographic detection of radioactivity (optional)
(0.5 hour)
EN 3 The cloud chamber   (0.5 hour)
EN 4 The ionisation produced by alpha particles
(optional)   (0.5 hour)
EN 5 Characteristics of a Geiger-Müller tube
(optional)   (0.5 hour)
EN 6 Penetrating power of ionising radiations   (1 hour)
EN 7 Variation of the intensity of gamma radiation with distance   (1 hour)
EN 8 The deflection of beta radiation by a magnetic field
(0.5 hour)

Note: experiments EN 4, EN 5, EN 6, EN 7 and EN 8 all require radioactive sources, GM tubes and counters.

Experiment EN 3 requires solid carbon dioxide.

References

Akrill	Chapter 19
Caro	Chapter 5
Duncan	Chapter 25
Muncaster	Chapters 52, 54
Nelkon	Chapter 35
Wenham	Chapter 46
Whelan	Chapter 64

2.1 Discovery

In 1896 the French physicist Henri Becquerel, while studying the phenomenon of phosphorescence, observed that compounds of uranium spontaneously emitted penetrating radiation. This radiation affected a photographic plate, like light, and ionised a gas, like X-rays. An element which emits this sort of radiation is said to be **radioactive.** Following this discovery, many scientists searched for other materials which were radioactive. One of the famous scientists in this field was Marie Curie; her work led to the discovery of the element radium, which is a million times as radioactive per unit mass as uranium . The photograph in figure 2.1 shows Marie and Pierre Curie.

There are many naturally occurring types of atom which emit radiation. Most of them are rare, but some are quite common, and expose us all to a low level of background radiation. One type of potassium atom, for example, is quite common in the earth. From there it passes through our drinking water into our bodies, where it remains.

Apart from naturally occurring sources of radiation, other radioactive sources are produced by 'atom smashing' particle accelerators and in nuclear reactors in power stations. All these sources emit, however, only three types of radiation. These are called alpha, beta and gamma radiations, and can be emitted with different energies, and in different combinations.

Marie and Pierre Curie

Figure 2.1

Q 2.1 Discussion question

Consult one of these references, or an encyclopaedia and prepare notes for discussion on the work of Becquerel and the Curies. To what extent were their discoveries dependent on
(i) chance,
(ii) what other scientists had discovered,
(iii) hard work? ∎

References

Bolton	Section 13.3
Caro	Section 5.1 and 5.2
Lewis and Wenham	Radioactivity
Romer	The restless atom

In this topic you will investigate the nature and properties of these radiations, partly by experiment. The possible hazards of radioactivity should, therefore, be considered.

2.2 Radiation hazards

All types of radiation carry energy. This can be released directly into the body or it can produce ionisation of substances in the body. These ions can disrupt the functioning of the body because they are chemically different. For example, about 70% of the human body is water. This can be ionised to form two highly reactive agents H^+ and OH^-.

Larger molecules such as RNA and DNA are even more easily damaged. The chemistry of the effect of these radiations on the human body is very complicated, but the following types of damage are known to occur at high doses.

(a) Large *molecules* cease to work; body chemistry is disrupted.

(b) All *parts of the cell*, especially chromosomes, can be damaged.

(c) The *whole cell* can be killed (radiation burn) or transformed into a state where it reproduces abnormally (i.e. becomes malignant).

(d) Certain *systems* in the body can be disrupted or become cancerous; examples are the central nervous system, intestine, and bone marrow (leukaemia).

(e) The above effects can lead to death.

In addition, it has been observed that genetic changes can occur in species as a result of chromosome damage.

Clearly, the danger from radiation is very serious. Under normal circumstances, everyone is exposed to low level background radiation. Some people may choose to undergo additional radiation for medical reasons. Such doses are carefully limited, and represent only a very small risk which is balanced against the potential benefit of the diagnosis or treatment.

Strict regulations govern the use of radiation sources in schools; the sources you will use in your experiments are very weak. The regulations insist on procedures being followed so that your exposure under normal circumstances will only be a few thousandths of the normal background radiation, averaged over any one year. A summary of these procedures is given in the *Student's resource book*. You should study these and discuss them with your teacher before starting the experiments, and refer to them whilst doing the experiments.

Q 2.2 Study question

List the sources of natural background radiation, and of manufactured sources. Without learning the details of units of dose or exposure, note down the relative size of the doses that you might typically be exposed to. ∎

Background reference
Living with radiation

You will realise from current concerns about nuclear power and nuclear weapons, that there is much still to be learnt about the precise nature of the biological effects of radiation and much disagreement about such information that is available.

The remainder of this topic and topics 4 and 5 will help you to understand and assess topical arguments and, we hope, develop an informed view of your own.

2.3 Detection of radiation

E Experiment EN 2 (optional)
Photographic detection of radioactivity

This experiment enables you to reproduce the observation of Becquerel, and fog a photographic plate, similar to that used

in a film badge for monitoring exposure in X-ray departments.

In this detector the radiations are releasing energy to discharge the ions in silver bromide and liberate metallic silver as the fogging. Almost all the other methods of detecting radiation use their ionising effect.

The cloud chamber

There are two types of cloud chamber, the expansion (or Wilson) and the diffusion (or Taylor) types. Both work on the same principle. Air containing vapour is cooled to a temperature at which the vapour will condense into droplets of liquid, if suitable condensation centres are available Such a vapour is said to be supersaturated. Ions are suitable condensation centres, so radiation which enters the cloud chamber and ionises the air in its path leaves behind a 'vapour trail'. This vapour trail gives information about the type of radiation which produced it.

Figure 2.2 shows the construction of a diffusion cloud chamber.

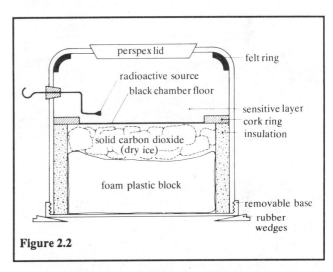

Figure 2.2

E Experiment EN 3
The cloud chamber

The aim of this experiment is to observe the tracks of different types of radiation in a simple diffusion cloud chamber.

Q 2.3 Study question

Make brief notes on the construction of the cloud chamber. Explain how the conditions for the formation of a supersaturated vapour are achieved, and how the tracks can be viewed. ∎

Q 2.4 Self-assessment question

Figure 2.3 shows the tracks in a cloud chamber produced by radiation from an alpha source.

(a) Which of the following do the visible tracks consist of?

A alpha particles
B ionised air molecules
C dust particles
D droplets of liquid

(b) The tracks are straight for most of their length, but slightly bent at the ends. Why do the tracks deviate from a straight line at the ends. ■

Figure 2.4 is a photograph of the tracks of beta particles. The thin line through the centre of the photograph is the track of a fast beta particle. The heavier curling tracks are due to slow particles.

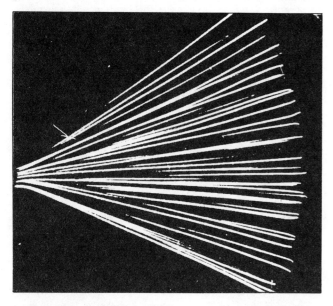

Figure 2.3

Figure 2.4

Q 2.5 Self-assessment question

(a) Why is the track of a fast beta particle fainter than the tracks of alpha particles?
(b) Why do slow beta particles produce such tortuous tracks?■

Ionisation chambers

These are devices which allow the amount of radiation to be measured, by measuring the charge produced by its ionisation. They are based on the same principle as the electroscope used in measurement of electrostatic charges.

Q 2.6 Self-assessment question

A radioactive source which emits alpha particles is placed inside the case of a gold leaf electroscope which is positively charged (figure 2.5). Explain why the leaf falls. ■

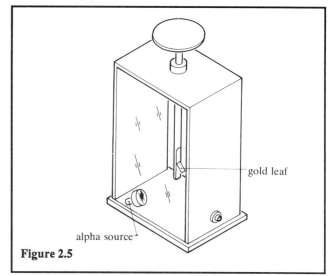

Figure 2.5

A simple form of ionisation chamber consists of two electrodes. Often the positive electrode (anode) is a cylindrical can, and the negative electrode (cathode) is a metal rod along the axis of the cylinder, as shown in figure 2.6.

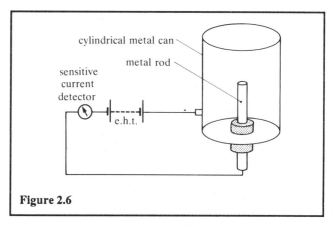

Figure 2.6

E Experiment EN 4
The ionisation produced by alpha particles

The aim of this experiment is to measure the ionisation current produced in air by radiation from a pure alpha source.

The Geiger-Müller tube

This is one of the most useful instruments for detecting radiation from radioactive elements. A typical Geiger-Müller (GM) tube is shown in figure 2.7. In the tube, which contains a gas at low pressure, a fine wire is maintained at a high potential with respect to the outer cylinder.

A high electric field is therefore set up in the vicinity of the central wire.

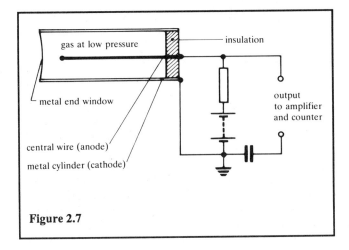

Figure 2.7

Q 2.7 Study question

The diagram (figure 2.8) shows an enlargement of the central wire of a GM tube and the track of a charged particle. The radiation ionises many gas atoms, one of which is shown in the diagram. There is a potential difference between the wire and the outer cylinder (not shown), the wire being positive with respect to the cylinder.

(a) In which direction will (i) the electron, and (ii) the positive ion, move under the influence of the electric field?
(b) Why do the electrons travel very much faster than the positive ions?
(c) How can the initial formation of a few ion pairs give rise to a very large pulse of current through the tube?
(d) Why is it important to absorb the energy of the positive ions? How is it achieved?
(e) What design modification would make a GM tube such as that shown in figure 2.7 suitable for detecting alpha radiation? ■

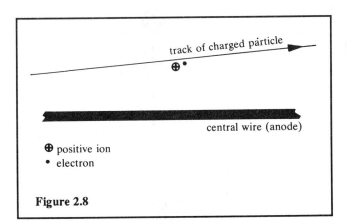

Figure 2.8

2.4 Properties of radiation

E Experiment EN 6
Penetrating power of ionising radiation

E Experiment EN 7
Variation of the intensity of gamma radiation with distance

E Experiment EN 8
The deflection of beta radiation by a magnetic field

The aim of these experiments is to investigate some of the properties of alpha, beta and gamma radiations quantitatively, using a GM tube as detector and a scaler or ratemeter for counting.

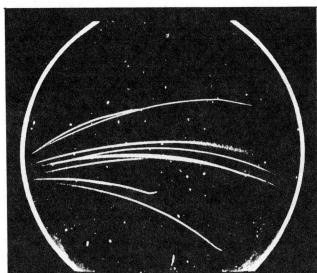

Figure 2.9

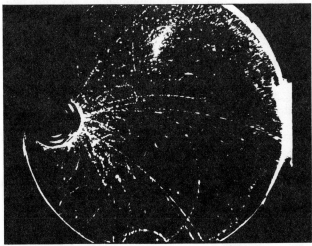

Figure 2.10

Behaviour in magnetic fields

Figure 2.9 shows the paths of alpha particles in a very strong magnetic field. The radioactive source is on the left of the photograph. The magnetic field is perpendicular to the plane of the photograph, and its direction is upwards, towards you.

Figure 2.10 shows the paths of β-particles in a magnetic field. Again, the source is on the left and the field is perpendicular to the plane of the photograph. This time, however, the field is directed downwards, away from you.

Q 2.8 Development question

Explain the following conclusions, drawn from study and comparison of the two photographs in figures 2.9 and 2.10.

(a) alpha and beta particles have opposite charges.
(b) alpha particles are more massive than beta particles (note the comparative strengths of the magnetic fields).
(c) The beta particles emitted from this source have different energies. ■

Q 2.9 Study question

Make notes on the properties of alpha, beta and gamma radiation under the following headings: range in air, ionising ability, effect of absorbing material, behaviour in electric and magnetic fields, speed. ■

Q 2.10 Self-assessment question

A radioactive source is placed 20 cm from a GM tube which is connected to a scaler. When a piece of lead 2 mm thick is placed between the source and the tube the count rate is equal to the background count. When the lead is removed, the count rate increases sharply. Which type of radiation is the source emitting? Give reasons for your answer. ■

Q 2.11 Self-assessment question

What relationship is there between count rate and distance from the source of gamma radiation in air? Does this relationship agree with the idea that the count rate is due to the emission of electromagnetic radiation from the source? ■

Q 2.12 Self-assessment question

The graph in figure 2.11 shows how many ion-pairs per mm are produced by an alpha particle at each point in its track.

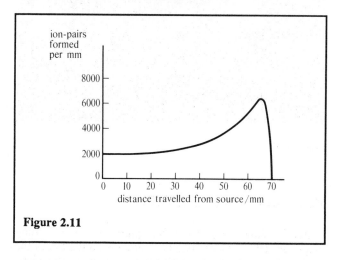

Figure 2.11

(a) Use this graph to estimate the number of ion pairs produced in the 70 mm track.
(b) How many fewer pairs would be produced in a 50 mm track?

(c) What is the total energy of an α-particle which produces a 70 mm track if 5×10^{-18} J is the average energy needed to produce an ion pair?
(d) Suggest why there is a peak near the end of the track. ■

The nature of alpha, beta and gamma radiation

A comparative study of the properties of alpha, beta and gamma radiation provides very strong evidence that alpha and beta are charged particles and gamma is a form of electromagnetic radiation. This is a familiar statement which you accept without question after seeing it so often in print; but try in this next section to examine the evidence about the nature of radioactive radiation as if you were one of the first investigators. The main evidence gathered by people like Rutherford is presented in the order in which it was obtained and you will be able to study their experiments and work through calculations using the results which they obtained. It should help to give you some insight into an exciting period of scientific history and an understanding of the knowledge which unfolded.

Nature of alpha particles

In 1902 (only six years after the discovery of radioactivity) Rutherford, working at McGill University, Montreal, began to test the view of Becquerel and Mme. Curie that 'alpha rays are charged bodies projected with great velocity'.

Figure 2.12 shows the arrangement of Rutherford's experiment. Alpha, beta, and gamma radiations were emitted from radium and its decay products in the source. The radiations could pass along narrow slits or channels between metal plates and through a very thin layer of aluminium (0.003 mm thick) to ionise the air in the electroscope causing the electroscope to discharge.

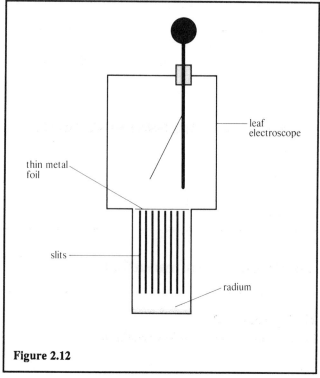

Figure 2.12

A variable magnetic field could be applied to deflect the alpha and beta particles so that they could not emerge from the slits and the alpha particles could also be stopped by covering the source with a plate of mica (0.1 mm thick). Rutherford made the following observations.

	Rate of electroscope discharge
(i) Without a magnetic field and with source uncovered	8.33 volts per minute
(ii) With a magnetic field strong enough to prevent beta particles emerging and with the source covered	0.92 volts per minute

Q 2.13 Development question*

(a) Why does the rate of discharge of the electroscope indicate the intensity of radiation reaching the source?
(b) Why are the slits in the form of long narrow channels?
(c) What causes the leaf to fall slowly in reading (ii)?

Rutherford removed the mica cover and increased the magnetic field until it was just strong enough to reduce the rate of discharge to 0.92 volts per minute once more. He knew that in this field the alpha particles were deflected just enough to prevent any from emerging.

(d) Sketch the path of an alpha particle which just fails to escape through the slit.

(*Hint.* Remember that the alpha particles will be emitted in all directions by the radium.)

Rutherford found that for his apparatus the radius of the circular track R_{max} discussed in part (d) was 0.46 m. If the particles were deflected with this curvature, none would escape through the slits. He obtained this effect with a magnetic flux density B of 0.84 T.

(e) Write down an equation relating the charge Q, mass m, velocity v, with B and R_{max} and calculate Q/m in terms of v.

The velocity of the alpha particles was estimated by using electric deflection to prevent them from emerging from the slits and this gave 2×10^7 m s^{-1} for the velocity of the alpha particles.

(f) Suggest how the slit system could be modified to provide electric deflection.
(g) Calculate Q/m for alpha particles from Rutherford's data. How does this value compare with Q/m for a hydrogen ion (9.6×10^7 C kg^{-1})? ■

In his conclusion to the experiment Rutherford wrote:

The value of Q/m for the alpha particle may be explained on the assumption that the alpha particle is (1) a molecule of hydrogen carrying the ionic charge of hydrogen, (2) a helium atom carrying twice the ionic charge of hydrogen, (3) one half of the helium atom carrying a simple ionic charge....

Even earlier than this he had written

I feel sure helium is the alpha particle .... My nose (which may be prejudiced) leads me to avoid the hydrogen molecule like the devil .... I shall cleave to helium if only for Galileo's doctrine of simplicity.

It comes as a surprise to hard-working A-level students that one of the aims of physicists is to make things simple! But Rutherford's work, above all, illustrates his belief that examination of complex and confusing data had to lead in the end to a simple and understandable pattern or model. He said more than once 'fundamental things have got to be simple' and his development of the simple nuclear model to account for the complex scattering effects of atoms shows how he successfully found this simplicity.

Not surprisingly, he pursued the most probable hypothesis (2) above and looked for a way of finding out the charge on a single alpha particle. In 1908, with Geiger, he found a way of counting alpha particles one by one, using a detector which was a very early form of the tube which Geiger and Muller developed later. They also measured the total charge on these particles by measuring the ionisation current produced by the alpha emission.

Results

1 gram of radium emits 3.4×10^{10} alpha particles per second. (3.7×10^{10} is now the accepted value.)
Charge on alpha particle = $+3.11 \times 10^{-19}$ C.

Rutherford found that radium was always slightly warmer than its surroundings because nuclear energy which is constantly being released by radioactive change is being absorbed as internal energy by radium. He found that this energy raised the temperature of radium by about 1.5 K above its surroundings, a rise which corresponds to an energy release of 0.12 J per second per gram of radium.

Q 2.14 Self-assessment question

(a) Using Rutherford's values of Q/m, Q, and v for alpha particles, calculate the mass and the kinetic energy of a single alpha particle emitted by radium.
(b) What energy is supplied to 1 gram of radium in each second if all the kinetic energy of the alpha particles is transformed into internal energy?
(c) Does this value account for the 1.5 K temperature excess of radium ? ■

The final experiment to obtain conclusive evidence about the identity of alpha particles was performed by Rutherford and Royds using the apparatus shown in figure 2.13. The alpha particles were emitted by radon gas in tube A which was surrounded by an evacuated tube B leading into a narrow discharge tube.

Q 2.15 Study question

Make brief notes on the Rutherford-Royds experiment explaining the design of the apparatus and the way it was used to confirm that alpha particles are helium nuclei. ■

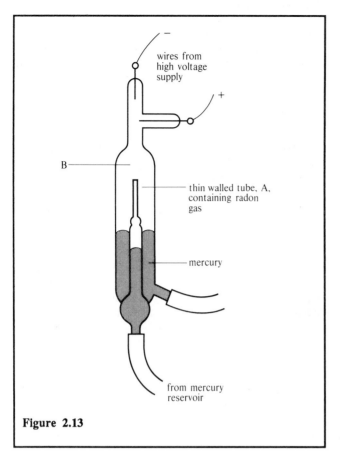

Figure 2.13

Nature of beta particles

In experiment EN 1 you measured e/m_e for electrons emerging from a gun with the same speed. To determine the nature of beta particles, it is necessary to measure their value of e/m_e but the experiment must be designed so that only beta particles of a particular speed pass through the deflecting fields.

In 1901 Kaufmann performed such an experiment and found that beta particles were emitted with varying speeds up to 95% of the speed of light. His results were as follows.

Speed of $\beta/10^8$ m s^{-1}	e/m for $\beta/10^{11}$ C kg^{-1}
2.36	1.31
2.60	0.97
2.85	0.63

We now know that the mass of a particle increases significantly as its speed approaches the speed of light (theory of relativity) and this accounts for the decrease in e/m_e at high speed.

At low speeds beta particles have the same values of e/m_e as slow electrons (-1.76 x 10^{11} C kg^{-1}) and so the evidence confirms that beta particles are high-speed electrons.

Nature of gamma radiation

If gamma rays are electromagnetic waves of similar wavelength and properties to short X-rays, two important experimental tests can be used to confirm this hypothesis.

Q 2.16 Self-assessment question

(a) What quantity is the same for all electromagnetic waves?
(b) What important property do X-rays exhibit as a result of their wave nature?
(c) Suggest two experimental tests which could be used to show that X-rays and gamma rays are similar kinds of radiation. ■

Q 2.17 Study question

Copy out the table 2.1 and fill in the numbered spaces. ■

Table 2.1 Properties of α, β and γ radiations

Property	alpha	beta	gamma
Affects a photographic plate	(1)	(2)	yes
Number of ion-pairs produced per mm in air (approximate)	10^4	10^2	1
Penetration (approximate)	10^{-2} mm of Al or several cm of air	(3)	(4)
Deflection by electric and magnetic fields	as negative charge, large deflection	(5)	(6)
Speed (approximate)	10^7 m s^{-1}	(7)	(8)
Mass	(9)	1/1837 that of a hydrogen atom	(10)
Charge	+2e	(11)	zero
Wavelength	-	-	10^{-10} to 2×10^{-13} m

Q 2.18 Self-assessment question

From your knowledge of the properties of alpha, beta and gamma radiation, state how the necessary laboratory safety precautions differ for the various types of radiation and assess the relative hazards of each type. ■

Photographic detection of radioactivity

Make sure you have read and understood the **safety rules** in the *Student's resource book* before you start this experiment.

Apparatus

○ dental X-ray film or bromide paper and 2 appropriate processing solutions
○ 3 x 50 ml beakers with cans to cover or 3 developing dishes
○ print tongs
○ timer
○ radioactive sources
○ handling tongs

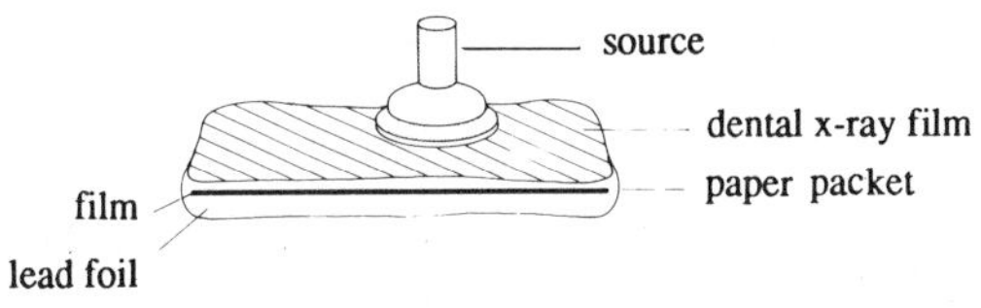

Figure 2.14

Procedure

If you are using bromide paper then the experiment must be set up and the processing done in a dark-room with a suitable safelight as the emulsion on the paper is very sensitive to white light.

The coating on the X-ray film incorporates a yellow filter so that it can be processed in subdued light.

1 Place the source(s) on the film pack as shown in figure 2.14 (or bromide paper) and leave for 15 to 20 minutes - exposure is not critical. If you use more than one source, make a note of each source and its position on the film or paper. The X-ray film may contain a lead foil screen so make sure the exposure is made on the front of the pack.

2 (a) Processing X-ray film

Set up the beakers containing developer, water and fixer. Working in subdued light and as quickly as possible, remove the yellow film from the pack and drop it into the developer and cover the beaker with a can. After a further 5 minutes wash the film and allow it to dry.

(b) Processing bromide paper.

Set up 3 dishes with developer, water and fixer. Slide the paper into the developer making sure the paper is completely covered. Develop for about 2 minutes. Keep the paper moving by rocking the dish gently.

Rinse the paper in water and place it in the fixer, again making sure the paper is completely covered with the solution. The time for fixing will depend on the type of fixer used.

Wash the paper for several minutes and then allow it to dry.

Note: The chemicals are safe to handle but it is advisable to use tongs and to wash your hands afterwards.

Questions

1 Compare the results obtained from different sources. Can you explain the difference in the results?

2 Are there any practical uses for this method of detecting radioactivity?

EXPERIMENT EN 3

The cloud chamber

Make sure you have read and understood the **safety rules** in the *Student's resource book* before you start this experiment.

Apparatus

○ diffusion (Taylor) cloud chamber kit
○ light source (with screening)
○ solid carbon dioxide (dry ice)
○ ethanol (e.g. surgical spirit)
○ dropping pipette
○ clean duster

1 Use a dropping pipette to put about 2 cm³ of ethanol on the felt strip inside the top of the cloud chamber, and replace the lid.

2 Put some dry ice (solid carbon dioxide) into the lower part of the chamber, cover it with the foam pad and screw the base back on. Put the cloud chamber in position on the bench, insert the radioactive source, and level the chamber with the rubber wedges included in the kit.

3 Position the lamp to illuminate a layer of cloud just above the floor of the viewing chamber.

4 Rub the top of the chamber with a wool cloth to charge it, as illustrated in figure 2.15. View the tracks produced by looking towards the light. The position of the lamp is critical, and should be adjusted until the tracks can be seen clearly.

Note. The chamber needs a minute or two to settle down, before clear tracks are produced. If the tracks do not appear, or become faint during the course of the experiment, (i) rub the top again with the duster, (ii) check the lamp position and re-adjust it if necessary, (iii) check the dry ice, which must be in contact with the floor of the viewing chamber to cool it properly.

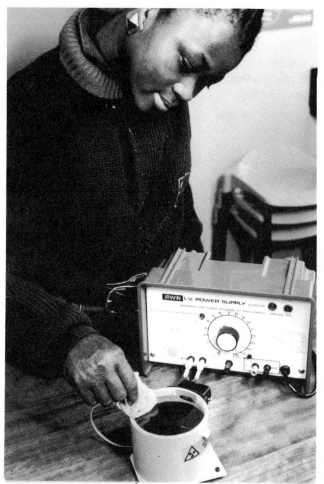

Figure 2.15

5 Describe and sketch the appearance of the tracks. How long are the tracks? Are they all the same length?

6 Place a piece of foil just in front of the source, and again observe the tracks.

7 What is the effect of the foil? Describe and sketch the appearance of any tracks which are visible.

Note. The tracks stopped by the foil are alpha particle tracks. The fainter tracks are produced by beta particles: you may need to black out the room and adjust the lamp position to see them. You may also see small bursts of condensation occurring without continuous tracks; these are due to gamma radiation.

EXPERIMENT EN 4

The ionisation produced by alpha particles

Make sure you have read and understood the **safety rules** in the *Student's resource book* before you start this experiment.

Apparatus

○ electrometer and meter
○ ionisation chamber to fit on the electrometer
○ alpha source (5 μCi)
○ e.h.t. supply, with meter
○ handling tongs
○ connecting leads

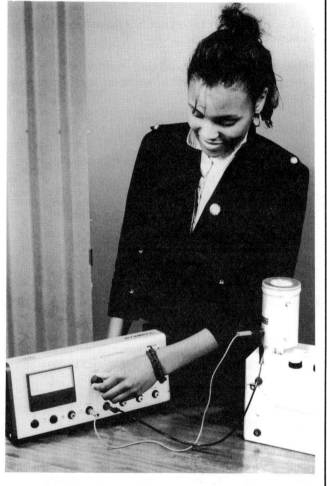

Figure 2.16

1 Read the instructions supplied with the electrometer, and use them to set up the electrometer and ionisation chamber as illustrated in figure 2.16.

Note. Although you are using a milliammeter to take readings, the readings themselves will be of the input voltage. This voltage is produced by the ionisation current, flowing in the input resistor that you selected.

2 Mount the source in the ionisation chamber and connect the e.h.t. supply, making the can positive. Increase the potential difference until all the ions which are being produced are being collected. This occurs when the reading on the meter will increase no further. The current then flowing is the ionisation current. Record the meter reading.

3 Calculate the ionisation current from the equation

$$\text{ionisation current} = \frac{\text{p.d. across input resistor}}{\text{input resistance}}$$

4 Calculate the number of particles produced by the source per second. The source strength is marked on the box containing the source, usually in microcuries, μ Ci.

Note. Most of the sources you use will be marked in microcuries, but the SI unit of source strength (activity) is the becquerel, symbol Bq. This unit is now coming into use. One becquerel is one emission per second and one curie which emits 3.7×10^{10} emissions per second is therefore 3.7×10^{10} Bq.

5 Calculate the total number of ions produced by the alpha particles per second if

$$\text{number of ions produced per second} = \frac{\text{ionisation current}}{\text{charge on ion}}$$

(the charge on one ion = 1.6×10^{-19} coulomb)

6 Calculate the number of ions produced by each alpha particle, using your results from the previous questions.

Characteristics of a Geiger-Müller tube.

The aim of this experiment is to find the correct operating voltage of the GM tube.

Make sure you have read and understood the **safety rules** in the *Student's resource book* before you start this experiment.

Apparatus

○ GM tube, suitable for detecting alpha particles
○ scaler
○ source of alpha radiation
○ stop-clock
○ handling tongs

Figure 2.17

1 Read the handbook for the counter (scaler or rateme-ter), or ask a teacher or laboratory technician to show you how it operates.

Note. The window on the end of the GM tube is very fragile. Do not touch it.

2 Set up the apparatus as in figure 2.17 with the source and the GM tube 10 cm apart, in line with each other, and firmly fixed. Set the voltage control to its minimum setting and switch on the counter.

3 With the scaler set to count, increase the voltage until counting starts. Record this voltage, and the count that occurs in 100 seconds. Calculate the number of counts per second, the *count rate*.

4 Increase the voltage by about 50 volts, and take another 100 second count. Repeat this to obtain a series of 100 second counts over a range of voltages.

Note. If the rate of counting starts to increase dramatically after remaining fairly constant for a few readings, do *not* raise the voltage any higher or the tube may be damaged.

5 Draw up a table of results, using three columns: one for the voltage, one for the 100 second count, and one for count rate. Plot a graph of count rate against voltage. Find out the manufacturer's recommended operating voltage for the tube you are using. Where does this voltage appear on your curve?

6 The graph of count rate against voltage has a 'plateau' region extending over a range of voltages. Why should the GM tube be operated at a voltage within this range?

EXPERIMENT EN 6

Penetrating power of ionising radiations

Make sure you have read and understood the **safety rules** in the *Student's resource book* before you start this experiment.

Apparatus

○ GM tube
○ scaler
○ alpha source
○ beta source
○ gamma source
○ range of absorbers (e.g. paper, aluminium of various thicknesses, lead of various thicknesses)
○ stop-clock
○ handling tongs

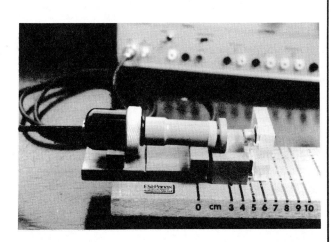

Figure 2.18

1 Connect the GM tube to the scaler. The voltage control should be set to the recommended operating voltage for your tube.

Figure 2.18 shows the GM tube connected to the scaler with a radioactive source and an absorber in position.

2 Measure and record the background count rate, in counts per minute. The counting period should not be less than five minutes.

3 What causes the background count?

4 Set up the alpha source 1 cm from the counter and record a one minute count.

5 Insert a sheet of paper between the source and the GM tube and repeat step four.

6 Remove the paper and gradually move the source away from the GM tube until the count ceases to fall. Record the distance between the tube and the source.

Note. If americium is the source, the count rate will not fall to background level because some gamma radiation is emitted. You can check whether any alpha radiation is still reaching the GM tube by putting a piece of paper in front of the source.

If the count rate drops when the paper is inserted, continue moving the source away from the tube until the insertion or removal of the paper does not affect the count rate.

7 How do the results of steps five and six compare with your observations of alpha tracks in a cloud chamber (experiment EN 3)?

8 Replace the alpha source with a beta source and repeat steps four, five and six. Use various thicknesses of aluminium as well as paper in step five. Record the thickness of aluminium necessary to absorb the radiation.

9 Replace the beta source with a gamma source and repeat steps four to six. Add various thicknesses of lead to the absorbers used in step five.

10 Which type of radiation is most likely to make up the background count? Why?

11 Use your results to explain the construction of the boxes in which the sources are stored.

EXPERIMENT EN 7

Variation of intensity of gamma radiation with distance

Make sure you have read and understood the **safety rules** in the *Student's resource book* before your start this experiment.

Apparatus

○ GM tube
○ scaler
○ gamma source
○ handling tongs
○ stop-clock

Figure 2.19

1 Set up the apparatus as shown in figure 2.19, but without a source in position. Set the voltage on the scaler to the operating voltage of the GM tube.

2 Take a 5 minute count of the background radiation. Record the background count rate in counts per 30 seconds.

3 Place the gamma source about 2.5 cm from the GM tube and take a 30 second count. Record the distance between the GM tube and the source, together with the 30 second count and the count rate deduced from it. Work out the net count rate, that is the count rate minus the background count rate, and record this as well.

4 Increase the separation between GM tube and source, and repeat step three.

5 Repeat step four until the count rate falls to little more than the background count rate. Draw up a complete table of results.

6 Plot a graph of count rate against distance, x.

7 Plot a graph of count rate against x^{-2}.

8 The points on the source holder and GM tube used to measure the separation x may not coincide with the active zones of each. Discuss the effect on the two graphs of such a systematic error in the value of x.

9 What is the relationship between the distance from a gamma source and the count rate, or intensity, experienced at that distance?

EXPERIMENT EN 8

The deflection of beta radiation by a magnetic field

Make sure you have read and understood the **safety rules** in the *Student's resource book* before you start this experiment.

Apparatus

○ GM tube
○ ratemeter or scaler and stop-clock
○ strontium 90 beta source
○ collimator for source
○ holders for GM tube and source
○ handling tongs
○ Eclipse Major magnet or strong bar magnet

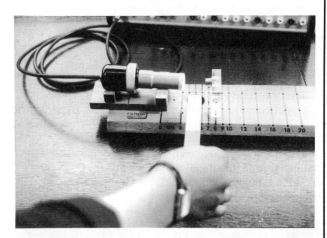

Figure 2.20

1 Place the source in the collimator, using tongs, and mount the collimator so that the slit is in line with the top edge of the GM tube window.

2 Set the ratemeter to 100 counts per second, with a short integrating time. (If you are using a scaler, take the count for one minute each time.)

3 Adjust the separation between the source and the GM tube until the count rate is about 40 per second (this will probably be when there is about 5 cm between the front of the collimator and the tube window). Measure and record the separation and the count rate.

4 Hold the magnet close to the end of the collimator, so that the field is horizontal and perpendicular to the line joining the source and the tube as shown in figure 2.20. Measure and record the count rate.

5 Reverse the poles of the magnet and take the new reading of the count rate.

6 From your readings, deduce which way the beta particles were deflected in each of the steps four and five. (If the count rate is lower than the reading in step three the deflection was upwards, and vice versa.)

7 Determine the direction of the field in steps four and five. (If the poles are not marked on the magnet, use a compass to identify them.)

8 Determine the sign of the charge on beta particles (from Fleming's left-hand rule, or by comparing your results with the deflection observed for a wire carrying a current in a known direction).

9 If a source was used which emitted beta particles with higher energies, how would the deflection differ?

Questions on objectives

1 Identify the type(s) of radiation, alpha, beta or gamma, which have the following characteristics:

(a) are *not* deflected in electric or magnetic fields,
(b) have a mass equal to that of an electron,
(c) are absorbed by a few mm of aluminium,
(d) have a mass about four times that of a hydrogen atom,
(e) can penetrate several inches of lead,
(f) have a charge of -*e*,
(g) have a maximum range in air of about 7 cm,
(h) consist of high frequency electromagnetic waves,
(i) have the same specific charge as electrons,
(j) are deflected towards the negative electrode in an electric field. *(objective 5)*

2 (a) Draw a labelled sketch of a Geiger-Müller tube which is suitable for detecting alpha particles.
(b) What is the reason for including a quenching agent in the gas filling of a Geiger-Müller tube? *(objective 3)*

Figure 2.21

3 A diffusion cloud chamber is set up in the usual way - a few drops of alcohol for the vapour, solid carbon dioxide for cooling, a radioactive source of 'luminous' paint, and a light source. Outline the adjustments you would make if no tracks appear in the chamber after a couple of minutes. *(objective 3)*

4 (a) Which radiation produced the tracks shown in figure 2.21?
(b) Why are the tracks of different lengths? *(objectives 4 and 5)*

5 'Alpha radiation is the most damaging to living tissue, but fortunately the one that we are least likely to be exposed to, under normal circumstances'. Explain this statement with reference to the properties of alpha radiation. *(objectives 5 and 6)*

6 'We cannot be fully protected from gamma radiation'. Is this true? What protection from gamma radiation would you recommend, from your experimental experience, and your knowledge of the properties of the radiation? *(objectives 4, 5, 6 and 7)*

TOPIC 3

The nuclear atom

Summary

This topic traces the development of the understanding of the atom brought about by experiments with very small particles. You will study the work of Rutherford and others, simulating a classic experiment in which the nucleus was discovered. You will learn about nuclear transmutations and can read, in an extension, of the complex tools used by the particle physicist.

Objectives

When you have completed the work in this topic you should be able to:

1 Use the following scientific terms correctly: nucleus, neutron, proton, nucleon, isotope, nuclide, scattering, inverse square law, positron, neutrino, nuclear transformation, artificial transmutation.

2 Define and use the following terms: nucleon number (mass number), proton number (atomic number), atomic mass unit.

3 State how many protons and neutrons there are in a nuclide for which you are given the symbol.

4 Describe the Rutherford model of the atom.

5 Perform and describe an experiment to illustrate nuclear scattering of particles by using a gravitational analogue.

6 Recall the size of a nucleus compared to that of an atom.

7 Interpret and construct equations representing nuclear reactions indicating the nature of the energy released.

8 Solve problems involving calculation of the relative abundance of isotopes.

9 Describe the construction and uses of a mass spectrometer and outline the principles involved.

1896	Becquerel	Discovery of radioactivity.
1897	Thomson	Identification of electron from deflection of cathode rays. Measurement of e/m for electrons.
1903	Rutherford	Measurement of e/m for alpha particles.
1909	Rutherford & Royd	Nature of alpha particles confirmed.
	Geiger & Marsden	Detection of large angle alpha particle scattering.
1913	Geiger & Marsden	Laws of alpha particle deflection determined, Measurement of size of nucleus.
1914	Rutherford	Existence of proton confirmed.
1919	Rutherford	Disintegration of nitrogen nucleus detected.
1925	Blackett	Nitrogen oxygen transmutation verified.
1932	Chadwick	Discovery of neutron.

Ernest Rutherford
(1871 — 1937)

EXTENSION

10 Describe methods of accelerating particles to high energy.

Experiments

EN 9 A gravitational analogue of nuclear scattering   (1 hour)

References

Akrill	Chapter 19
Caro	Chapters 8, 10, 11, 12, 13 and 14
Duncan	Chapters 22 and 25
Muncaster	Chapters 48 and 51
Nelkon	Chapter 35
Wenham	Chapters 47 and 48
Whelan	Chapter 63

3.1 The discovery of the nucleus

Following his discovery of the electron, as described in topic 1, J.J. Thomson compared the specific charge of an electron with that of an ion. He came to the conclusion that the residual part of an atom must be much more massive than an electron, and have a positive charge. Thomson suggested an arrangement within the atom thus:

'In default of exact knowledge of the nature of the way in which positive electricity occurs in the atom, we shall consider a case in which the positive electricity is distributed in the way most amenable to mathematical calculations; i.e. when it occurs as a sphere of uniform density throughout which the corpuscles (electrons) are distributed (J.J. Thomson 1907).

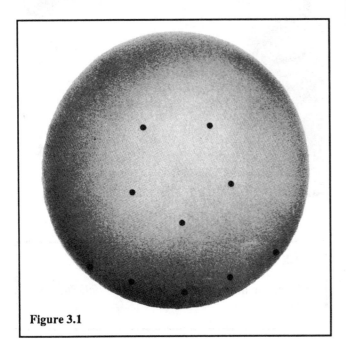

Figure 3.1

This has become known as the 'raisin' or 'plum pudding' model of the atom (figure 3.1). Thomson was able from this to explain radioactive disintegration, and develop some links with the periodic table of elements. In the search for quantitative support for this model, he considered what would happen if alpha particles were passed through thin metal foils. The prediction, using the plum pudding model, was that they would undergo very little scattering from their original path.

Rutherford was working at Manchester in 1909, having already established a high reputation for his discoveries in the field of radioactivity. Working with Geiger, he had observed that alpha particles could pass through thin metal foils with very little scattering, which supported Thomson's predictions. However, he suggested that a student, Marsden, might see if they could be scattered through a larger angle. As Rutherford later recalled:

'Then I remembered two or three days later Geiger coming to me in great excitement and saying, 'We have been able to get some of the α-particles coming backwards...' It was quite the most incredible event that has ever happened to me in my life. It was almost as incredible as if you fired a 15-inch shell at a piece of tissue paper and it came back and hit you'.

The experiments designed by Geiger and Marsden have since become famous for their simplicity and their impact on our ideas of the structure of the atom. They resulted in Rutherford publishing, in 1911, what might be called the 'planetary' model of the atom. This was radically different from Thomson's model, and has been the basis for all later developments. The main feature of the model is that the atom has a small central nucleus in which the positive charge and mass are concentrated. Electrons are in orbit around this nucleus (figure 3.2).

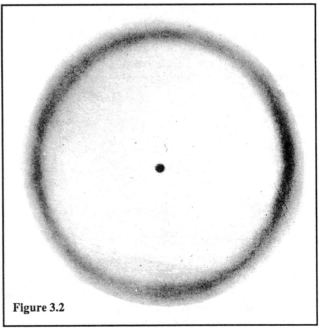

Figure 3.2

The diameter of the atom is about 10^5 times that of the nucleus; a typical nucleus is 10^{-15} m across, compared to the diameter of a typical atom which is 10^{-10} m. Most of the atom's volume is thus almost empty space. To give an analogy; if the nucleus were the size of a large full stop, the diameter of the atom would be bigger than the height of a 15 storey block of flats. (A large full stop is 0.5 mm across, the height of a block of flats is about 50 m.)

Q 3.1 Self-assessment question

If the nucleus were represented by an orange of 10 cm diameter, what object would correspond in height to the diameter of the whole atom? ■

Q 3.2 Discussion question

Do you find the analogy of the previous question helpful? Why is this so? Can you devise some similar analogies for the very large, very small or otherwise difficult to visualise? ■

Background reference
Houwink's *Sizing up science* is packed with this kind of comparison; you will find much in it to surprise and entertain you.

It is not possible to carry out the alpha scattering experiment in the laboratory. The following questions are designed to help you study the original and prepare for a simulation, experiment EN 9.

Q 3.3 Study question

Write a brief account of the experimental arrangement used by Geiger and Marsden. ■

Q 3.4 Study question

How did the results of the scattering experiment support Rutherford's model of the atom and show that the Thomson model was incorrect? ■

Q 3.5 Self-assessment question

If an α-particle penetrates very close to the central nucleus of an atom, what force will be acting on it? Why can the force due to the electrons be ignored? ■

The repulsive force between a positively charged gold nucleus and a bombarding α-particle (helium nucleus) is proportional to $1/r^2$ (r being the distance between the centres of the two nuclei).

Q 3.6 Self-assessment question

(a) What is the relationship between r and the electric potential at different places in the field around the gold nucleus?
(b) What will happen to the energy of a bombarding α-particle as it approaches the gold nucleus? (You should discuss how its potential energy changes as it approaches this nucleus.) ■

Similar changes will occur in the energy of a moving ball as it climbs up a hill in a gravitational field, and if the hill is shaped so that the height is proportional to $1/r$ (see figure 3.3) the hill will provide an exact gravitational analogue of the repulsive electric field around a nucleus. If results show that a moving ball is deflected by this hill in the way that α-particles are deflected by gold nuclei, we can obtain clear support for the idea that α-scattering is produced by an electrically charged nucleus.

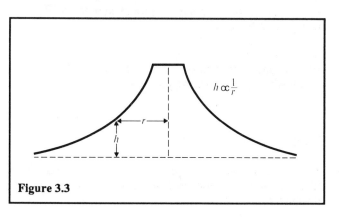

Figure 3.3

E Experiment EN 9
A gravitational analogue of nuclear scattering

In this experiment you will find how the number of particles scattered in different directions is distributed and compare the results for the gravitational analogue with the results of Geiger and Marsden.

C Computer program
Particle scattering

This is a simulation in which you have to infer the nature of an unknown object from its effect on a beam of particles.

Q 3.7 Self-assessment question

(a) Copy figure 3.4a and complete the diagram to show how two α-particles of the same energy but different aiming error p_1 and p_2 are scattered by a gold nucleus.
(b) Figure 3.4b shows the path of an α-particle near a gold nucleus. Copy this diagram and show on it the path of another α-particle with the same aiming error but less energy. ■

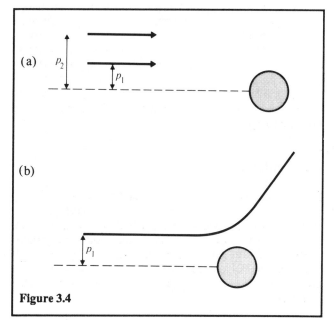

Figure 3.4

Q 3.8 Self-assessment question

(a) Write down an expression for the electric potential at a point distance r from the centre of a gold nucleus (charge of gold nucleus = 79e).

(b) What electrical potential energy will an α-particle have at distance r from the centre of the gold nucleus (charge of α-particle = 2e).

(c) Calculate how close an α-particle of energy 8 x 10^{-13} J (5 MeV) will come to a gold nucleus in a head-on collision assuming that the gold nucleus acquires no kinetic energy during the collision.

$$(e = 1.6 \times 10^{-19} \text{ C}; \ 1/4\pi\varepsilon_o = 9 \times 10^9 \text{ N m}^2 \text{ C}^{-2}.)$$

Hint. Remember that when a ball is rolled up a hill to simulate a head-on collision, it stops momentarily when it acquires potential energy equal to its original kinetic energy. ■

The radius of the nucleus must be *less* than this distance of closest approach. The actual size of a nucleus will be calculated in topic 5.

3.2 Structure of the nucleus

The proton

The structure of the nucleus was a problem which occupied Rutherford for many years. In 1919 he bombarded nitrogen gas with alpha particles from a radium source, and detected a penetrating radiation. To explain his observations, he suggested that an alpha particle had been captured by a nitrogen atom, producing an unstable nucleus which rapidly changed with the emission of a proton.

Q 3.9 Self-assessment question

Why is a proton a more penetrating radiation than an α-particle? ■

These observations supported two important propositions:
(i) Protons must be one of the constituents of the nucleus.
(ii) There must be a strong attractive force in the region of the nucleus. Nuclei and alpha particles are both positively charged, and positive charges repel each other according to the inverse square law (as in the scattering experiment). For an alpha particle to be captured there must be another force acting, besides the electric force of repulsion, very close to the nucleus. This short-range attractive force is called the **nuclear force.**

The neutron

In 1932 Chadwick was working at the Cavendish laboratory where Rutherford was the director. He investigated the radiation produced when alpha particles bombarded beryllium, which was even more penetrating than the protons emitted from nitrogen. Chadwick discovered that this radiation consisted of particles with almost the same mass as protons, but with no charge. These particles are called **neutrons.**

Q 3.10 Self-assessment question

Why is it difficult to detect neutrons? ■

Neutrons are also constituents of the nucleus, and protons and neutron are known collectively as nucleons. They are held together in the nucleus by the nuclear force. The number of neutrons in a light nucleus is almost the same as the number of protons, but the ratio of neutrons to protons increases as the number of protons increases. This ratio determines the stability of the nucleus. An unstable nucleus is radioactive, and by emitting alpha and/or beta particles becomes more stable.

Proton number

The **proton number** of an element is equal to the number of protons in the nucleus. Therefore, it is also equal to the number of electrons in a neutral atom, which determines the chemical nature of the element. Thus, in effect, the proton number defines the chemical characteristics of an atom and the place of the element in the periodic table. This number, which is represented by the symbol Z, is sometimes still referred to as the atomic number.

Nucleon number

The **nucleon number** is equal to the sum of the number of protons and neutrons (that is, the number of nucleons) in the nucleus. The nucleon number is represented by the symbol A and is sometimes still referred to as the mass number.

In general, an atom can be represented as

$$\text{nucleon number} \longrightarrow {}^{A}_{Z}X \quad \text{chemical symbol}$$
$$\text{proton number} \longrightarrow$$

This symbol ${}^{A}_{Z}X$ represents a nuclide; a particular proton-neutron combination of a given chemical element.

The simplest nucleus is that of hydrogen, which consists of a single proton. The nuclide of hydrogen can be written as

$${}^{1}_{1}\text{H.}$$

Helium has two protons and two neutrons, and can be represented by

$${}^{4}_{2}\text{He.}$$

Q 3.12 Self-assessment question

A nuclide of fluorine has an proton number of 9 and a nucleon number of 19.

(a) Write the nuclide symbol.
(b) How many protons are there in the nucleus?
(c) How many neutrons are there? ■

Nuclear mass

We will now consider ways of *comparing* the masses of different atoms and ions and of measuring atomic masses absolutely in kilograms.

Relative atomic mass is the term now used in preference to the old name 'atomic weight'.

$$\text{relative atomic mass} = \frac{\text{mass of atom}}{\frac{1}{12}\text{ mass of }{}^{12}_{6}\text{C atom}}$$

The carbon atom is taken as the standard because it is very stable and is contained in many substances, e.g. all organic matter. The mass of an atom is sometimes expressed in terms of the atomic mass unit (1 u).

1 u is defined such that the mass of carbon-12 is 12 u.

There are many ways of comparing the masses of different atoms, e.g. by comparison of gas densities, or by measuring changes in mass produced by chemical changes.

Q 3.13 Self-assessment question

Suggest how measurements of the mass of hydrogen liberated during electrolysis can be used to measure the mass of a single hydrogen ion. What other information is required to calculate the result? ■

Isotopes - the mass spectrometer

Thomson's experiments in 1913 on the deflection of positive ions confirmed the existence of **isotopes** first suggested by Soddy in 1910 as he studied radioactive decay. He was forced to conclude that sometimes several substances were produced, all occupying the *same place* in the periodic table but differing in atomic mass, e.g. radon-222 and radon-220. 'It is impossible to believe', he said 'that the same may not be true for the rest of the periodic table'. The mass spectrometer has clearly verified this prediction of the existence of isotopes, not just of unstable radon but of stable neon, oxygen, etc.

A mass spectrometer consists of three essential parts.

1 An ion source which converts atoms or molecules into ions and accelerates them to produce a beam of high speed ions which can be deflected by electric or magnetic fields;

2 An analyser for separating the ions into a mass spectrum;

3 An ion detector - this may be a photographic plate or an ion collector connected to an electron multiplier and amplifier to make it so sensitive that it can detect and measure minute traces of an isotope (as small a proportion as 1 part in 10^7).

Q 3.15 Self-assessment question

Figure 3.6 represents the ion source of a mass spectrometer.

(a) Why are electrons fired into the space beween plates X and Y?
(b) Plate Y is made very slightly more negative than X. What is the effect of this?
(c) There is a p.d. of about 1000 V between Y and Z, and Z is more negative than Y. What happens because of this p.d.?

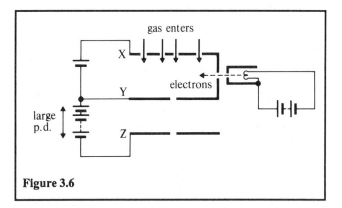

Figure 3.6

(d) Assuming that the ions emerging from the slit in Z carry the same charge, which of the following must also be true? (i) The ions have equal masses, (ii) the ions have equal energy, (iii) the ions have equal velocity? Give a reason for your answer. ■

In one form of mass spectrometer developed by Bainbridge (figure 3.7 p34) the ions from the source first pass through a velocity selector before being deflected by a magnetic field through 180°.

EXTENSION

Positive rays

While Rutherford and his colleagues were investigating the structure of atoms and nuclear charge, J.J. Thomson was doing experiments to study the properties of 'positive rays'. These were streams of positive ions produced in a discharge tube containing low pressure gas. The ions were produced by collisions between electrons and gas atoms and the stream of positive ions accelerated to the cathode where they passed through a narrow channel into an evacuated glass tube (figure 3.5). By deflecting the positive ions in electric and magnetic fields, J.J. Thomson was able to measure the specific charge for the ions.

Q 3.14 Self-assessment question

(a) Why do the ions passing through the cathode have different speeds?
(b) Which ions will be deflected most by the fields - fast or slow ions?
(c) What are the directions of deflection of the ions due to (i) the electric field and (ii) the magnetic field shown in figure 3.5? ■

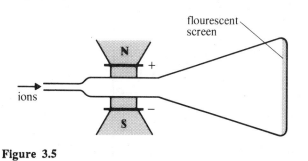

Figure 3.5

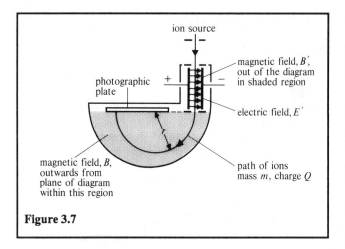

Figure 3.7

In the velocity selector, the ions carrying charge Q experience forces due to a magnetic field B and an electric field E between the parallel plates. Only those ions which experience zero net force emerge from the last slit.

Q 3.16 Self-assessment question

(a) Derive an equation for the speed v of the ions emerging from the velocity selector in terms of B' and E'.
(b) If the magnetic field in the velocity selector is 0.20 T, what p.d. must be applied between the plates (separation 10 mm) to enable ions of velocity 1.7×10^5 m s^{-1} to emerge?
(c) If ions of mass m emerge from the selector, move with speed v and are deflected into a circular path, radius r, by the deflecting magnetic field (flux density B) find a relationship for Q/m.
(d) If ion velocity and magnetic flux density are fixed, how does the radius of the path depend on the ion mass m? ∎

The table 3.1 show some naturally occurring isotopes and indicates their relative abundance. The study of nuclear structure, through bombardment by high energy particles, had led to a great increase in the number of discovered isotopes (1500 nuclides at the last count!) of varying stability produced by nuclear transformation and realising the dream of the ancient alchemists.

Table 3.1 Some naturally occurring isotopes showing relative abundance.

	%		%		%
$^{1}_{1}H$	99.98	$^{16}_{8}O$	99.76	$^{112}_{50}Sn$	1.1
$^{2}_{1}H$	0.02	$^{17}_{8}O$	0.04	$^{114}_{50}Sn$	0.8
$^{6}_{3}Li$	7.9	$^{18}_{8}O$	0.20	$^{115}_{50}Sn$	0.4
$^{7}_{3}Li$	92.1	$^{20}_{10}Ne$	90.00	$^{116}_{50}Sn$	15.5
$^{12}_{6}C$	98.9	$^{21}_{10}Ne$	0.27	$^{117}_{50}Sn$	9.1
$^{13}_{6}C$	1.1	$^{22}_{10}Ne$	9.73	$^{118}_{50}Sn$	22.5
$^{14}_{7}N$	99.62	$^{35}_{17}Cl$	75.5	$^{119}_{50}Sn$	9.8
$^{15}_{7}N$	0.38	$^{37}_{17}Cl$	24.5	$^{120}_{50}Sn$	28.5
				$^{122}_{50}Sn$	5.5
				$^{124}_{50}Sn$	6.8

Q 3.17 Self-assessment question

Chlorine with relative atomic mass 35.5 has two isotopic forms $^{35}_{17}Cl$ and $^{37}_{17}Cl$. Calculate the relative abundance of these two forms in naturally occurring chlorine. ∎

Isotopes cannot be distinguished by chemical properties because all isotopes of the same element have the same number of extra-nuclear electrons and it is these electrons which determine chemical properties. We have seen, however, that isotopes can be separated by magnetic deflection which depends on the mass of the ions.

Q 3.18 Study question

Suggest other properties which depend on mass and say how they might be used in separating isotopes. ∎

Summary of terms

The constituent particles (protons and neutrons) of all nuclei are called **nucleons.**

The number of protons is the **proton number** (or atomic number) Z.

The total number of nucleons is called the **nucleon number** (or mass number) A

The neutron number $N = A - Z$

A particular nuclear species with a unique pair of values of Z and N is called a **nuclide.**

Nuclides of a given element having different nucleon numbers (mass numbers) are called **isotopes** of the element.

3.3 Nuclear transmutations

Bombarding atoms with α-particles was the first of many different methods used not only to create new elements but to find out the constituent particles of the nucleus and to learn about the forces within the nucleus. The five discoveries mentioned in this section are important breakthroughs in this search.

In each case you should notice: (i) The ways in which the experimenters knew that the transformation of matter had occurred; (ii) The hypothesis that was proposed to explain the change; and (iii) how this hypothesis was tested and other hypotheses ruled out.

Nuclear transmutations can be represented in two ways:

(i) by an equation in which the total nucleon number and total proton number balance on each side; (ii) by a symbolic expression of the form

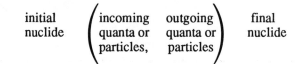

The proton

Rutherford's discovery of this particle, by the bombardment of nitrogen gas with α-particles was mentioned in the previous section, as a vital link in understanding the nature of the nucleus.

Q 3.19 Self-assessment question

Complete the equation representing the change caused in Rutherford's bombardment.

$$^{14}_{7}\text{N} + ? \rightarrow ^{18}_{9}\text{F} \rightarrow ? + ? \ \blacksquare$$

Q 3.20 Study question

(a) Find out what observations were made and explain how these fitted the suggestion that a proton had been produced.
(b) How did a cloud chamber photograph later confirm the correctness of Rutherford's hypothesis? ■

The neutron

It was discovered that when α-particles bombarded beryllium a radiation was produced which could penetrate several centimetres of lead. When this 'beryllium radiation' passed through a block of paraffin wax, very high speed protons were produced. Figure 3.8 represents the experimental arrangement used by Chadwick in 1932 to investigate the mystery.

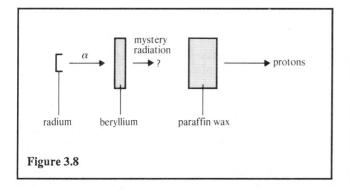

Figure 3.8

Q 3.21 Study question

(a) Some scientists suggested that the unknown radiation was high energy γ-radiation. How is it possible to estimate the energy of γ-rays?
(b) Why did Chadwick reject the idea that the unknown radiation might be γ-rays? ■

Q 3.22 Self-assessment question

(a) Chadwick suggested that neutrons (neutral particles of approximately the mass of a proton) were emitted from the beryllium. Complete his equation: ■

$$^{9}_{4}\text{Be} + ? \quad ? + ?$$

(b) What is likely to happen to the energy of a neutron after a head-on collision with a proton (hydrogen nucleus) in the wax?

(*Hint.* Neutrons and protons have similar masses.) ■

So nuclear bombardment has produced emissions of both protons and neutrons from the nucleus - the two constituent particles of all nuclei. The neutron itself has been found to be unstable outside the nucleus decaying with a half-life of 13 minutes into a proton and an electron. What happens within the nucleus is even more a matter for conjecture though we know that certain nuclei emit β-particles. This β-emission must be the result of the decay of a neutron into a proton with the ejection of an electron.

The positron

In the same year that the neutron was discovered, Anderson in California discovered yet another particle. The photograph (figure 3.9) shows the curved tracks of a particle in a cloud chamber moving in a magnetic field which is directed *into* the plane of the paper. It is not possible to say how the particle is charged unless its direction of travel is known.

Q 3.23 Development question*

(a) If the particle has a negative charge, which way is it moving through the chamber?

Anderson put a lead plate in the chamber which caused a change in the curvature (figure 3.9).

(b) How does the presence of the lead plate determine the direction of travel?
(c) What kind of charge does the particle carry? ■

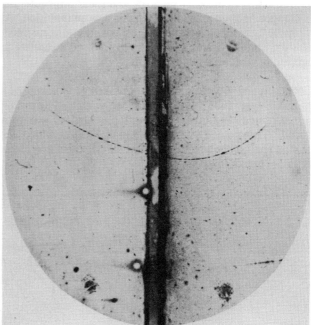

Figure 3.9

Measurements showed that the particle had a value of specific charge equal to that of an electron but its charge was positive - the existence of the positron was confirmed.

Artificial radioactivity

The French physicists Frédéric and Irène Joliot-Curie found that when they bombarded aluminium with α-particles they obtained neutrons.

Q 3.24 Self-assessment question

(a) Complete the expression for this change.

$$^{27}_{13}\text{Al}(^{4}_{2}\alpha, \,^{1}_{0}\text{n})\ldots$$

(b) They found that as a result of the nuclear transformation the GM tube gave a count and went on counting even after the α-source had been removed. However, this count rate fell to half in 3.5 minutes.

What can you deduce from these results?

(c) The radiation detected by the GM tube could pass through a thin sheet of aluminium but was stopped by a similar thickness of lead. The decay process led to the formation of an isotope of silicon ($Z = 14$, $A = 30$). Write down an equation to describe the change and state what kind of radiation is emitted. ■

The Joliot-Curies received the Nobel Prize in 1935 as the discoverers of the first artificial radioactive isotope.

Splitting the atom

With the discovery of the neutron, the α-particle lost its unique status as the only high speed nuclear projectile, the uncharged neutron providing valuable new ammunition. At the same time, the first high voltage machines were invented, like the van de Graaff generator, and helped scientists to accelerate protons to high speeds.

Cockcroft and Walton, in 1932 at Cambridge, bombarded a lithium target ($^{7}_{3}\text{Li}$) with high speed protons. The proton was captured and a transitory unstable nucleus was produced. This nucleus split into identical halves which exploded apart and were detected by scintillations and cloud chamber tracks (figure 3.10).

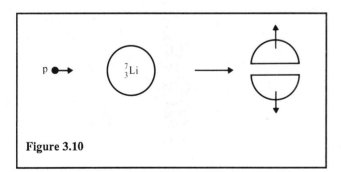

Figure 3.10

Q 3.25 Self-assessment question

Say what particles were detected and write down an equation representing the change. ■

This experiment was the first in which a large nucleus was split. The experiment is also significant for the following reasons:

(1) According to the conventional laws of physics, it should not have happened. The proton did not have enough energy to overcome the potential barrier of nuclear repulsion and only the later wave mechanics theory suggested that there was a small probability of the proton reaching the nucleus.

(2) Energy appeared to have been created. The emitted α-particles had more energy than the original proton. We look for an explanation of this in the next topic.

Arranging for small particles to collide at ever increasing energies has been one of the most fruitful, if expensive, fields of physics in this century. This has led not only to a fuller understanding of the atom, but also of the forces which shape all matter and events.

By the late 1930s, the nucleus was supposed to contain or emit the following particles: proton, neutron, electron (ß), positron, neutrino, π-meson (having positive and negative forms).

Between 1945 and 1963 about 100 more 'elementary' particles had been discovered but not how they were related nor the fields connecting them.

Matter can no longer be distinguished from the fields that connect it. The present view is that the massive particles (protons, neutrons, pions, etc.) are composed of 'truly' elementary quarks held together by gluons (massless and corresponding to, or making up, the field).

The process of collision in increasingly powerful accelerators seems to create an endless proliferation of particles. A 40 TeV US collider is planned for 1996.

We need a theory (the real objective of physics) to make order (the real objective of people) to make a pattern of these phenomena. There are four forces at work in nature, four fields that affect particles: the strong nuclear, the electromagnetic, the weak nuclear and the gravitational. (Some evidence for a fifth, and possibly a sixth force, both gravitational, is emerging.) To connect them all we need a Grand Unified Theory (GUT).

Background Reading

Calder, R. 'Man and the Cosmos', 1968. Penguin. Chapter 12.
Gardner, 'The Ambidextrous Universe', 1967. Penguin. Chapters 20-24.

C Comprehension EN 2
The electron probes the universe

This article is about an up-to-date version of 'atom-smashing' - the way in which electrons can be fired into matter at high energies, and the information the resulting collisions give about the fundamental particles of matter.

3.4 Particle accelerators

Cockcroft and Walton in 1932 showed how a proton of energy 250 keV could unlock some of the secrets of the nucleus. So began an era of research using particle accelerators as one of the basic tools to probe the nucleus and discover the elementary particles of matter. The nations of Europe have now pooled their resources to build a 28 GeV accelerator at CERN, Geneva. In 45 years, the energy given to the bombarding particle has been multiplied by a factor of over 100 000.

The simplest way to give energy to a charged particle is to accelerate it through a high voltage as is done in TV sets, mass spectrometers, etc. Accelerating machines enable this process to be repeated again and again. Two methods of producing this repeated acceleration are outlined below and the CERN accelerator incorporates both methods to produce high energy protons.

The linear accelerator

The **linear accelerator** principle is illustrated by figure 3.11a. A line of metal tubes are connected as shown to a high voltage alternating supply and placed in an evacuated tube. Figure 3.11b shows the electric field along part of the accelerator.

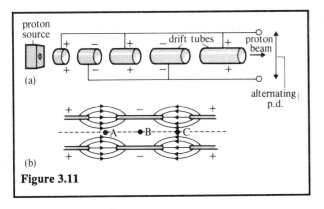

Figure 3.11

Q 3.26 Self-assessment question

(a) If a proton moves along the axis from left to right, what change, if any, do you expect in each of the regions A, B, C?
(b) What is the net effect on the proton's velocity caused by its passage from A to C?
(c) While the proton is drifting at constant velocity in the field-free region inside a tube (e.g. B) the voltage supply changes its polarity (tubes which were positive become negative). What will now happen as the proton moves between tubes at C?
(d) What difference do you notice in successive drift tubes? What is the reason for this?

(e) If the potential difference between successive tubes is 50 keV, what is the net gain in energy (in electron volts) of a proton which emerges from an accelerator, after crossing ten gaps?
(f) If the proton is to reach an energy of 1 MeV, how would you modify the accelerator? Would you (i) increase the length of the drift tubes, (ii) use more drift tubes, (iii) increase the voltage between the drift tubes, (iv) make the whole accelerator twice as long ?

Say if any of these suggestions are inappropriate and give a possible solution. ∎

The sheer size and cost limit the maximum energy obtainable from a linear accelerator and the longest in the world accelerates electrons to energies of 3.2×10^{-9} J (20 GeV) after travelling three kilometres!

The proton synchrotron

The proton synchrotron allows high energies to be achieved more economically by arranging a series of accelerating cavities in a circle of constant radius. In the linear accelerator, the distance between accelerating gaps is made progressively bigger so that the particle does not get out of step with the alternating voltage. This is not possible in the synchrotron because the particles travel through the same cavities many times at different speeds (figure 3.12).

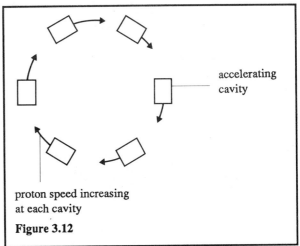

proton speed increasing at each cavity

Figure 3.12

Q 3.27 Self-assessment question

(a) How is it possible to keep the changes in alternating voltage in step (i.e. synchronised) with the arrival of the particle at the accelerating centres?
(b) The establishing of a magnetic field provides the centripetal force to enable the particle to move in a circle. What must we do to the magnetic field if the particle increases its speed yet remains on the path of constant radius? ∎

continued

EXTENSION

The synchrotron can produce a package of high energy particles accelerated during a small interval. During this period the magnetic field progressively increases and the frequency of the alternative voltage supply increases until the magnetic field cannot increase further. Then the particles are deflected out of the circle onto the target by applying a local magnetic field at the target exit tube.

Figure 3.13 shows how protons in the CERN accelerator are accelerated in three steps:

(i) to an energy of 0.55 MeV by the p.d. between the ion source and the end of the accelerator;
(ii) to 50 MeV by a linear accelerator;
(iii) to 28 GeV by a synchrotron.

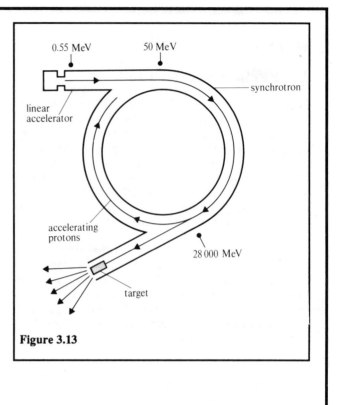

Figure 3.13

A gravitational analogue of nuclear scattering

Apparatus

○ alpha scattering analogue
○ graph paper
○ drawing board
○ wedges, 4
○ spirit level
○ carbon handwriting paper (pen type) or lycopodium powder

Figure 3.14

Procedure

Set up the apparatus as shown in figure 3.14. Make sure that the drawing board is level. The carbon paper should be placed on the paper which is attached to the drawing board in such a way that a trace can be obtained of the path of the ball as it leaves the hill, or sprinkle lycopodium powder on the paper to show the track of the ball.

Adjust the position of the chute and the height of the ball so that for an aiming error of 10 mm the scattering angle is about 120°. This initial height of the ball on the chute must be kept constant throughout the experiment. Roll the ball down the chute at various aiming errors p between 10 mm and 60 mm and record the corresponding scattering angles ϕ. You will find that there is a considerable spread in the scattering angle at large angles, so you should take several readings of ϕ for each value of p and find the mean path taken.

Results

Record in a table the aiming error p and the scattering angle ϕ.

p	ϕ	p^2	corrected p^2

Calculate the values of p^2. The last column will be completed later.

In order to compare the experimental results for the mechanical model with those of the α-particle scattering experiment, it is necessary to know how many particles are scattered at more than each angle ϕ.

An α-particle A in figure 3.15 aimed at a distance p from the nucleus would be scattered through an angle ϕ. Particle E would be scattered through an angle less than ϕ. All particles B, C, D which are aimed at a distance smaller than p would be scattered at an angle greater than ϕ. All particles scattered by more than ϕ would pass through an area πp^2. The number of such particles must be proportional to p^2.

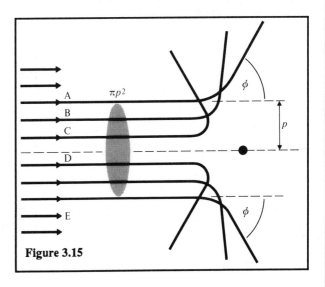

Figure 3.15

continued

EXPERIMENT EN 9

Testing the analogue by graph

If the hill is a good model, the relation between p^2 and the angle ϕ for the hill should be the same as the relation between the *number of α-particles* scattered through more than ϕ and the angle ϕ. The data calculated from Geiger and Marsden's results is given in table 3.2.

Table 3.2

Angle $\phi/°$	Numbers proportional to number of particles scattered at more than ϕ
120	154
105	266
90	448
75	767
60	1 384
45	2 811
30	7 725
15	458 000

Plot a graph of number of α-particles scattered at more than any angle ϕ (y-axis) against the angle ϕ (x-axis).

A graph of p^2 against ϕ for measurements made with the hill should have just the same shape as the graph from Geiger and Marsden's data for α-scattering.

However, the two sets of data have to be brought onto a common scale. To do this, we will make the two sets of results fit at one point and then see if the rest fall into line.

From your results select p_1, one value of p which produces a scattering angle of between 25° and 40°. We will call this angle ϕ_1. (Select a value of scattering angle ϕ_1 in the middle of the curve.) From your graph record N_1, the number of particles which are scattered through an angle of more than ϕ_1 (see figure 3.16). To make the vertical scale the same for both sets of results, the values of p^2 must be multiplied by a factor k.

$$k = \frac{N_1}{p_1{}^2}$$

Calculate k. Record the corrected values of p^2 where corrected $p^2 = k \times$ actual value of p^2.

Plot a graph of the corrected p^2 against ϕ on the graph of number of α-particles scattered at more than any angle ϕ against ϕ (using the same axes).

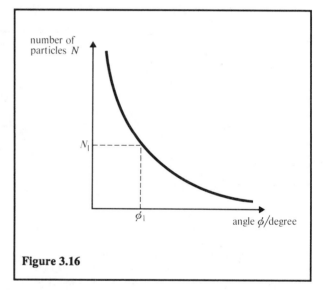

Figure 3.16

Conclusions

Compare the graph you have obtained from the analogue experiment with the graph you have plotted from Geiger and Marsden's results. Say whether your results support the speculation that an α-particle is scattered near a nucleus by an electrical force which varies as $1/r^2$.

Questions on objectives

1 Name the sub-atomic particle which has
(a) unit positive charge,
(b) unit negative charge,
(c) no charge.   *(objective 1)*

2 The term nucleon refers to
A protons
B neutrons
C protons and neutrons
D protons, neutrons and electrons   *(objective 1)*

3 A radioactive isotope of iodine can be represented by the symbol $^{131}_{53}I$.

(a) How many protons are there in this nuclide?
(b) How many neutrons are there in this nuclide?
                                        (objective 3)

4 Approximately what fraction of the *volume* of an atom is occupied by the nucleus?
A 10^5
B 10^{-1}
C 10^{-5}
D 10^{-15}

5 When a thin foil of gold is bombarded with alpha particles, why do only a very small proportion get deflected through more than 90°?   *(objective 4)*

6 (a) Why was it necessary to carry out the scattering experiment in an evacuated chamber?
(b) How were the alpha particles detected?   *(objective 5)*

7 (a) Figure 3.17 shows the tracks of four α-particles scattered at different times by the same gold nucleus. Copy the sketch and mark in a likely position for the nucleus. How did you choose this position?
(b) Calculate the closest distance of approach for an α-particle with energy 5 MeV if it travels head-on to the nucleus. (Assume the gold nucleus is very massive.)
(Charge on gold nucleus $79e$, $e = 1.6 \times 10^{-19}$ C,
$1/4\pi\varepsilon_o = 9 \times 10^9$ N m^2 C^{-2}.)
(c) Use your answer to (b) and your sketch in (a) to estimate how far the 'edge' of the atom will be from the nucleus on your scale diagram if the radius of a gold atom is 3×10^{-10} m.
                                        (objective 5)

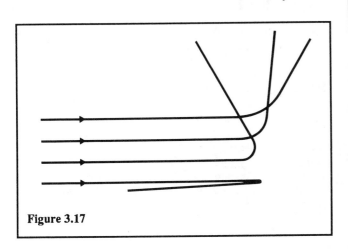

Figure 3.17

8 Give the missing terms in each of the following reactions:

(a) $^{27}_{13}Al + {}^{4}_{2}He \longrightarrow {}^{1}_{1}H + ()$

(b) $^{11}_{5}B + {}^{4}_{2}He \longrightarrow {}^{14}_{7}N + ()$

(c) $^{24}_{12}Mg(----,{}^{1}_{1}p)^{24}_{11}Na$

(d) $^{27}_{13}Al\,({}^{1}_{0}n,----)^{28}_{13}Al$ *(objective 7)*

9 Magnesium has three stable isotopes ^{24}Mg, ^{25}Mg, ^{26}Mg and the relative abundances are 79%, 10%, 11%. What would be the relative atomic mass from a chemical determination?
                                        (objective 8)

---

10 EXTENSION

Figure 3.18 represents two parallel horizontal metal plates between which a uniform electric field is maintained. X and Y are two fine slits at the same horizontal level. The assembly is inside a vacuum enclosure, which also contains a source of positive ions that directs a beam of positive ions into X along the line XY. The ions in the beam have various masses, charges and velocities.

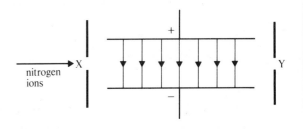

Figure 3.18

(a) Show that, with a uniform magnetic field of suitable flux density B normal to the plane of the paper applied over the whole of the region between the plates, all the ions which have the same velocity (whatever the charge) can be made to travel along the straight line XY and emerge from Y. If v is chosen to be 1.0×10^4 m s^{-1} and E is 2.0 kV m^{-1}, what is the necessary value of B?
(b) The beam of selected velocity v passes out through Y into a uniform magnetic field directed at right angles to the path. If v is 10^4 m s^{-1} and the flux density of this applied magnetic field is 0.060 T, find the radius of the circular path described by a ^{14}N$^+$ nitrogen ion of specific charge 1.14×10^6 C kg^{-1}.
(c) The ions ^{15}N$^+$ and ^{14}N^{2+} are also present in the ion beam of (b).
Find the specific charge of each of these ions and the radii of the paths which they describe. State briefly how each of these ions differs in structure from the ^{14}N$^+$ ion.   *(objective 9)*

Decay and use of radioisotopes

Study time: 1.5 weeks

Summary

This topic brings together the ideas of the two previous topics. You will study what happens to a nuclide when it gives out radiation and how the decay of a radioactive source proceeds. You will review the wide range of uses of radioisotopes and assess the potential hazards.

This photograph shows the Turin shroud which was believed to be the burial cloth of Christ but radiocarbon analysis has shown that it is dated from the 13th century A.D.

Objectives

When you have completed the work in this chapter you should be able to:

1 Use the following scientific terms correctly: radioisotope, exponential decay/growth, radioactive disintegration, daughter nuclide, activity, exposure.

2 Define and use the term half-life.

3 Indicate the nuclide produced from a given nuclide by a stated decay process and describe this using symbols for the nuclides and radiations involved.

4 Explain the origin of alpha, beta and gamma decay by consideration of the unstable nucleus.

5 Perform and describe an experiment to determine the half-life of a radioactive substance which is of the order of minutes.

6 Solve numerical problems on half-life.

7 Relate, in simple terms, the random nature of an individual disintegration to the steady decay of a radioactive source.

8 Define and use the term radioactive decay constant.

10 State the radioactive decay law as an equation and solve numerical problems using it.

11 Describe three uses of radioisotopes.

12 Identify the factors which determine the potential hazards of radioisotopes and evaluate the appropriateness of safety precautions, in qualitative terms.

Experiments

EN 10 Radioactive decay - half-life.   (1 hour)
EN 11 Monitoring radiation   (0.5 hour)

References

Akrill	Chapter 19
Caro	Chapter 5
Duncan	Chapter 25
Muncaster	Chapter 52
Nelkon	Chapter 35
Wenham	Chapter 46
Whelan	Chapter 64

4.1 Types of decay

Radioactivity involves the nucleus of the atom, and can be thought of as an attempt by an unstable nucleus to become more stable. This can be achieved by the emission of either an alpha particle or a beta particle from the nucleus.

Either process may be accompanied by the emission of gamma rays. The result is the formation of a nucleus of an atom of a different element, as shown in figure 4.1.

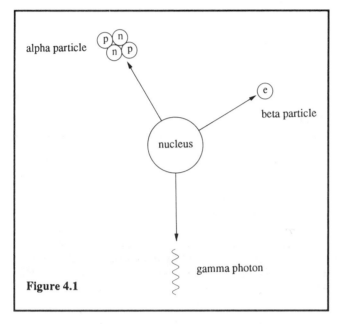

Figure 4.1

Alpha decay

An alpha particle is a helium nucleus, with two protons and two neutrons, and can be represented by the nuclide symbol $^{4}_{2}$He.

Radium is an element which emits alpha particles. One isotope of radium is $^{226}_{88}$Ra.

Q 4.1 Self-assessment question

(a) How many protons are there in the nucleus of radium-226?
(b) How many neutrons are there in this nucleus? ∎

The nuclide formed by the alpha decay of radium-226 (the daughter nuclide) is radon, Rn. This change can be written as

$$^{226}_{88}\text{Ra} \rightarrow {}^{222}_{86}\text{Rn} + {}^{4}_{2}\text{He}$$

In the change from radium to radon, the nucleon number has decreased by four and the proton number by two. The element formed is, therefore, two places lower in the periodic table. In general terms, if the initial nuclide has the chemical symbol L and the daughter nuclide is M, the equation for alpha decay is

$$^{A}_{Z}\text{L} \rightarrow {}^{A-4}_{Z-2}\text{M} + {}^{4}_{2}\text{He}$$

Beta decay

A beta particle is a fast-moving electron of either negative (β^-) or positive charge (β^+).

Note. Since beta (-) decay is the most frequent mode of decay in beta emission, the term beta decay usually implies the emission of electrons.

When beta (-) decay occurs, a neutron changes into a proton and an electron. The proton stays in the nucleus and the electron is emitted as as beta (-) particle.

Strontium (Sr) has an isotope which decays by the emission of beta (-) particles to yttrium (Y). The equation for this change is

$$^{90}_{38}\text{Sr} \rightarrow {}^{90}_{39}\text{Y} + {}^{0}_{-1}\text{e}$$

In this case, the nucleon number has remained the same and the proton number has increased by one. The element formed is one place higher in the periodic table.

In general, if an element Q changes to an element R by emission of beta (-) particles, the equation for beta decay is

$$^{A}_{Z}\text{Q} \rightarrow {}_{Z+1}^{A}\text{R} + {}^{0}_{-1}\text{e}$$

Beta (+) or positron emission results from the decay of a proton into a neutron and a positron. The neutron stays in the nucleus and the positron is emitted as a beta (+) particle.

Carbon has an isotope which decays into boron by the emission of a beta (+) particle. The equation for this change is

$$^{11}_{6}\text{C} \rightarrow {}^{11}_{5}\text{B} + {}^{0}_{+1}\text{e}$$

In this case the proton number has decreased by 1 and the nucleon number stays the same.

In general, if an element X changes to an element Y by the emission of beta (+) particles the equation for beta (+) is

$$^{A}_{Z}\text{X} \rightarrow {}_{Z-1}^{A}\text{Y} + {}^{0}_{+1}\text{e}$$

Gamma decay

This process may be explained by considering that nuclei (as well as atoms) have certain fixed energy states. That is, the energy of the nucleus can take only certain values. When alpha or beta particles are emitted the nuclei may be left in an excited state, with extra energy. This excess energy is removed by the emission of gamma rays when the nuclei return to their lowest energy state (the ground state).

The daughter atom formed by radioactive decay may itself be unstable, and decay further by any of the means already described. Many elements may thus be formed from one 'parent' element with an unstable nucleus.

The disintegration process can continue through several stages before a stable nucleus is produced. Naturally occurring radioactive nuclides can be classified into three decay series; the uranium, actinium and thorium series. In experiment EN 11 you will study the decay of protactinium 234 which is part of the decay series which starts with uranium 238.

Q 4.2 Study question*

(a) Write the equations for the uranium decay series, from $^{238}_{92}U$ to $^{234}_{92}U$.

(b) Write the equations of two different schemes by which $^{214}_{83}Bi$ could decay into $^{210}_{83}Bi$, using the table of elements in table 4.1. ■

Table 4.1

Element	Symbol	Z
thallium	Tl	81
lead	Pb	82
bismuth	Bi	83
polonium	Po	84

4.2 Half-life

The emission of an alpha particle from a radium nucleus happens spontaneously; it is beyond control. Radioactive disintegration is unaffected by the chemical or physical states of the radioactive sample. For example, there is a radioactive isotope of carbon, $^{14}_{6}C$, which is used for archaeological dating. It is believed to be formed in the upper atmosphere by the action of cosmic rays. The carbon-14 nuclide then forms radioactive carbon dioxide, which spreads through the atmosphere. Carbon containing a constant proportion of carbon-14 is transferred through photosynthesis into plant cells, and so also into animals. All living things contain carbon with the same proportion of carbon-14 as the atmosphere. When a plant or animal dies, its carbon atoms no longer get replaced. The carbon 14 continues to decay, and the proportion present gradually decreases. This is the basis of the dating method. In all these forms, the probability of distintegration of the nuclide is unchanged.

The precise moment when a particular nucleus will decay cannot be predicted; some atoms of radium may exist for thousands of year, whereas others may decay within a few seconds. The atoms decay quite randomly, as if someone were tossing a coin or throwing dice to decide which should decay at a particular instant. We cannot predict that a five will turn up when a die is thrown. All we can say is that there is one chance in six, or a probability of one-sixth, that a five will be thrown. Similarly, chance determines the behaviour of radioactive atoms.

If we assume that all atoms have the same chance of decaying within a certain time, we can use statistical methods to obtain an expression for the 'average life-time' of an atom. Since even a small radioactive source contains a vast number of atoms, the predictions of probability will be more accurate than those which can be made about the fall of dice.

The quantity which is used for describing the radioactive decay of an element is called the half-life, $T_{1/2}$. The half-life is the time in which half of all the nuclei that were originally present change into other stable or unstable nuclei. This is shown in a simplified form for a small number of atoms in figure 4.2.

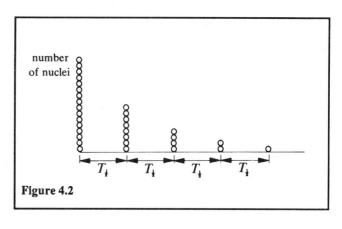

Figure 4.2

E Experiment EN 10
Radioactive decay - half-life

The decay of a radioactive substance is simulated by hand-throwing dice, and by a computer program which does a similar operation on a larger scale. The experiment which follows is a determination of the half-life of either protactinium-234 or radon-220.

Q 4.3 Self-assessment question

A radioactive isotope has a half-life of 15 minutes.
(a) How many half-lives does it have in one hour?
(b) What fraction of the original number of nuclei would remain after one hour?
(c) What fraction of the original number of nuclei would have decayed after two hours? ■

Q 4.4 Self-assessment question

Two radioactive elements L and M have half-lives of 25 minutes and 50 minutes respectively. Samples of L and M initially contain the same number of atoms. What is the value of the fraction

$$\frac{\text{number of atoms of L unchanged}}{\text{number of atoms of M unchanged}}$$

after 100 minutes?

A   4
B   2
C   1
D   1/2
E   1/4 ■

The half-lives of different isotopes vary enormously, from millionths of a second to thousands of millions of years. Each isotope, however, has a characteristic half-life, which can be determined experimentally.

This can be an important means of identification.

4.3 Exponential decay

Experimentally determined curves for the decay of radioactive isotopes, such as protactinium-234, show that the half-life is, within experimental uncertainty, the same at different parts of the curve (figure 4.3).

This type of curve is called a constant ratio curve. That means that in equal intervals of time it drops by the same ratio. So, in figure 4.4, OB/OA = OC/OB = OD/OC. This type of curve arises whenever the rate of change of something (such as the rate of disintegration of radio-

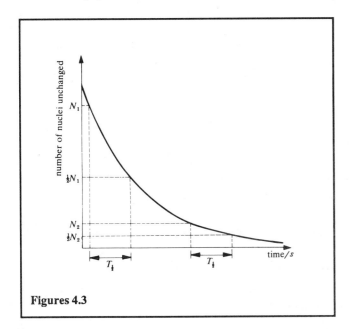

Figures 4.3

active nuclei) is proportional to how much there is of that something (such as the number of nuclei present). It is known as an **exponential** curve.

A radioactive substance decays exponentially with time; this is the radioactive decay law.

Q 4.5 Self-assessment question

Which of the curves A to E in figure 4.5 show exponential changes? ■

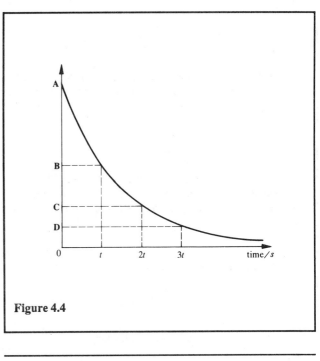

Figure 4.4

C   Computer program
NUCLEI

This program simulates the rate of decay of a radioisotope, showing how random processes can lead to a predictable outcome.

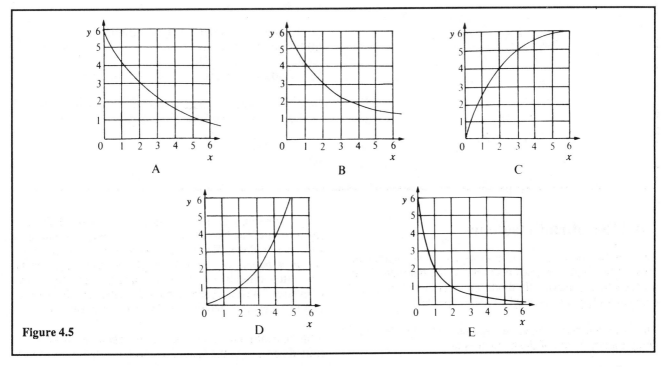

Figure 4.5

EXTENSION

A mathematical treatment of radioactive decay

If the rate of disintegration of a given nuclide at any time is directly proportional to the number of nuclei present, then

$$\frac{\mathrm{d}N}{\mathrm{d}t} \propto N$$

where N is the number of nuclei present and $\mathrm{d}N$ is the number decaying in the infinitesimal time interval $\mathrm{d}t$. Writing this as an equation,

$$\frac{\mathrm{d}N}{\mathrm{d}t} = -\lambda N$$

where λ is a constant of proportionality called the radioactive decay constant. The negative sign is necessary, if λ is to be a positive constant, because N decreases as t increases.

Integrating this equation gives

$$\int \frac{\mathrm{d}N}{N} = -\int \lambda \, \mathrm{d}t$$

$$\ln N = -\lambda t + \text{constant}$$

Note. The symbol ln means natural logarithm, that is, logarithm to the base e.

If there are N_o undecayed nuclei at time $t = 0$, then

$$\ln N_0 = 0 + \text{constant}$$

Therefore $\ln N = -\lambda t + \ln N_0$

$$\ln N - \ln N_0 = -\lambda t$$

$$\ln \frac{N}{N_0} = -\lambda t$$

$$\frac{N}{N_0} = e^{-\lambda t}$$

$$N = N_0 \, e^{-\lambda t}$$

This equation expresses the decay law mathematically; that is, a radioactive substance decays exponentially with time.

The relationship between λ and $T_{1/2}$ can be derived, since at $T_{1/2}$ the original number of nuclei N_o has reduced to one half, $N_o/2$.

Since

$$\frac{N}{N_0} = e^{-\lambda t}$$

when

$$N = N_0/2 \quad \text{and} \quad t = T_{\frac{1}{2}}$$

$$\tfrac{1}{2} = e^{-\lambda t}$$

taking logs to base e,

$$\ln \tfrac{1}{2} = -\lambda T_{\frac{1}{2}}$$
$$\lambda T_{\frac{1}{2}} = -\ln \tfrac{1}{2}$$
$$= \ln 2$$
$$= 0.693$$

Therefore $T_{\frac{1}{2}} = \dfrac{0.693}{\lambda}$

Both λ and $T_{1/2}$ are characteristic for a nuclide.

Q 4.6 Self-assessment question

The half-life of thoron is 52 s. Calculate its decay constant . ■

Q 4.7 Self-assessment question

1 g of radium $^{226}_{88}$Ra emits 3.7 x 10¹⁰ alpha particles per second.

Estimate

(a) the number of atoms in 1g of radium.
(b) the decay constant of radium.
(c) the half-life $T_{1/2}$.
(The Avogadro constant = 6.0 x 10²³ mol⁻¹).■

Note. Exponential change is also covered in the mathematics section of the *Student's resource book*.

4.4 Uses of radioisotopes

The number of known radioisotopes is now approaching 2000. Some radioisotopes occur naturally, but many of the most useful are artificially produced by bombarding a stable element with neutrons or with charged particles.

Their uses are many and varied, and new uses are continually being found. Some of the main ones are:

1. **Energy sources.** The large-scale generation of electricity from nuclear fission and fusion is covered in the next topic and in the option *Energy and its uses* in the *Student's resource book*. On a much smaller scale energy can be converted directly to electricity using a thermoelectric converter. These are used in 'nuclear' batteries which power heart pacemakers, navigational beacons and satellites.

Although radium-containing luminous paint is not now permitted because of the hazard, emergency lighting in hospitals, for example, can be powered directly from radiation by a similar process of luminescence.

2. **Sterilisation.** Medical equipment can be sterilised by exposure to gamma radiation, which destroys surface bacteria.

3. **Radiotherapy.** Gamma rays from radioisotopes are increasingly used in place of X-rays for the treatment of cancer. These can be administered by exposure from an external source or from substances taken into the body when the treatment is called 'chemotherapy'.

4. **Testing and quality control.** In the manufacturing industries radioisotopes are used for many purposes, from detecting cavities in castings to estimating the number of pills in a box.

5. **Studying dynamic systems.** The introduction of a small amount of a radioactive substance called a **tracer** into systems such as plants, water flows, etc. enables changes and flow patterns to be studied.

6. **Medical diagnosis.** A radioisotope tracer is introduced into the patient, where it undergoes the same chemical changes as the stable isotope of the same element, but can be detected by its activity showing up details of the body's functions and abnormalities (figure 4.6).

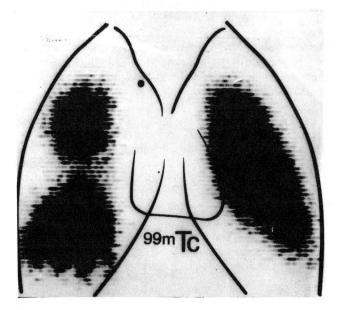

Figure 4.6

Assessing the hazards

The types of damage caused by radiation were discussed in topic 2. The degree of hazard depends on a number of factors about the source of radiation and the situation in which the body is exposed.

1) Type of radiation emitted

α, β or γ (X-rays have very similar effects to γ).

2) Energy of radiation

All types can be emitted with different energy, depending on the radioisotope; more energetic radiations are more penetrating.

3) Amount of radioisotope

The greater the quantity, the greater the number of disintegrations (called the activity of the source) which produce radiation.

4) The half-life of the source

This will determine the period over which the radiation is emitted, and the level of activity at any time.

5) The physical nature of the source

Solid or sealed sources can only affect from outside the body. Powders, liquids and gases can be taken into the body and irradiate it for as long as they remain as contaminants.

6) Protective screening

Exposure from external sources can be reduced by screening. Lead is particularly effective, and necessary for handling gamma sources, which are most penetrating. Thick leaded glass is used for windows in concrete enclosures in which these sources are manipulated (figure 4.7).

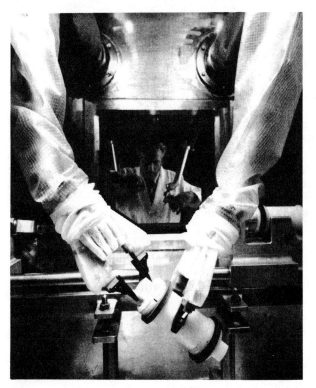

Figure 4.7

7) Biological interactions

Some substances will be excreted fairly quickly from the body, e.g. iodine. Others, such as plutonium, remain for a long time.

8) Type of body tissue exposed

Different parts of the body are not equally affected by the same exposure. In general, those tissues in which the cells are rapidly reproducing, for example, the skin, gut, bone-marrow and reproductive organs, are most affected. Muscles are less affected, and the brain which does not grow after maturity, least affected of all.

Q 4.8 Self-assessment question

(a) Why may a radioactive gas be potentially more hazardous than a solid source?
(b) Why do you think that the source used in your school laboratory which generates thoron gas is relatively harmless although it emits α-particles.
(c) How is the exposure from the stronger 'sealed' sources used in the laboratory, kept low? ■

E Experiment EN 11
Monitoring radiation

Each of the two experiments will require about half-an-hour to set up and they can then be left running. The aim of EN 11 (a) is to monitor this radiation over a period of 1 day. With EN 11(b) the aim is to show that emission rates are never constant and to illustrate the random nature of radioactive decay.

Q 4.9 Study question

Write a summary of the factors affecting the potential hazards of radioisotopes, based on the section you have just read. Give an ionising radiation, indicating how these factors are taken into account. ■

It will be clear that it is a difficult matter to devise satisfactory precautions, to take account of all these factors, in the very wide range of uses of radioisotopes. In practice, there is a whole range of precautions, practices and permitted dose rates. These are considered in some detail in the option *Medical physics* in the *Student's resource book*. Two examples are given here.

The ideal radiopharmaceutical

In order to minimise the hazards this will have the following properties:

(a) it will follow only the metabolic pathways which it is wished to study (e.g. iodine 131 for thyroid function);
(b) it will be a pure γ emitter;
(c) it will have a half-life of about one-and-a-half times the duration of the investigation (e.g. technetium 99m has a half life of 6 hours);
(d) it will emit γ-rays at energies of moderate energy (100-500 keV), neither too high to be imaged, or so low that most of the energy is absorbed by the body;
(e) it will not be toxic.

Q 4.10 Self-assessment question

Explain why the above properties will reduce the dangers of the radioisotope to the patient. ■

The next question shows how a radioactive isotope can be used to measure the volume of blood in a patient without having to drain it off! It illustrates how radiation can be used effectively and without any anticipated harmful effects.

Q 4.11 Self-assessment question

A small volume of a solution containing a radioactive isotope of sodium with an activity of 12 x 10³ disintegrations per minute is injected into the bloodstream of a patient. After 30 hours, the activity of 1.0 cm³ of the blood is found to be 0.50 disintegrations per minute. If the half-life of the sodium isotope is 15 hours, estimate the volume of blood in the patient's body. Mention possible sources of error. ■

Radioactive waste

The use of radioisotopes produces waste in a number of ways. Materials used to handle radioisotopes, such as rubber gloves, paper towels, glassware, etc., become contaminated; these are called **low-level wastes**. The materials are usually incinerated and the ash buried. The activity from these wastes is a small fraction of natural background radiation and constitutes negligible risk. Waste also arises from radioisotopes which have decayed to a level which makes them unusable in their original situation, for example, fuel rods in a power station. In addition, these rods and other used radioisotopes may have decayed to different unstable nuclides, which will present different hazards. These are the **intermediate** and **high level wastes**. The dangers will depend on the half-lives, but also on the amounts produced. Where these are large, as in the nuclear power industry, the dangers can be reduced by:

(i) leaving the rods in cooling ponds for a period of time so that short-lived high activity isotopes decay;
(ii) reprocessing to produce the longer-lived isotopes in a more suitable form for disposal, whilst extracting the undecayed uranium isotopes for re-use.

You will know that the plans of the Central Electricity Generating Board to dispose of these wastes by burial has aroused opposition and controversy. Many people say of the wastes 'Not in my backyard!' Figure 4.8 illustrates the presence of radioactive substances in a suburban garden.

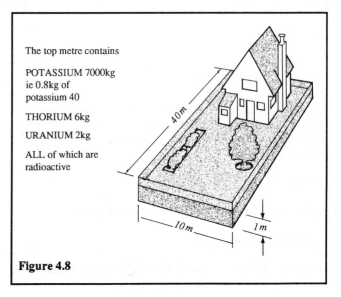

The top metre contains

POTASSIUM 7000kg
ie 0.8kg of
potassium 40

THORIUM 6kg

URANIUM 2kg

ALL of which are
radioactive

40m

10m

1m

Figure 4.8

Q 4.12 Study question

How do the risks from nuclear power station waste compare with the natural radiation in your 'backyard'? ■

Background reference
Your radioactive garden, Lord Marshall of CEGB.

Q 4.13 Discussion question

EITHER

With other members of your class or group, prepare a debate on the benefits and dangers of using radioisotopes.

OR

Adopt the roles of the various people and agencies that would be involved in a plan to bury waste at a particular site. The lesson could take the form of a public enquiry with each interested party having prepared a short paper appropriate to their role, e.g. CEGB physicist, Greenpeace activist, local conservationist, etc. ■

Background references

There is a large output of books and leaflets from organisations involved, in addition to articles in the Press, and textbooks. The following are particularly recommended:

Living with Radiation from NRPB is a useful introduction to the quantitative aspects of radiation hazards and protection.

Nuclear Energy by Robin McKie gives a brief, easy to read, introduction to most of the arguments for and against nuclear power generation.

Nuclear Power, Man and the Environment by R.J. Pentreath is a comprehensive account of the nature of radioactivity and its effects on humans and on the environment.

EXPERIMENT EN 10

Radioactive decay

In this experiment you should do the simulation of EN10A part 1 and preferably then 2, and then one of the parts of EN10B depending on apparatus available.

A Analogues

1 Hand-thrown dice

Apparatus

○ 100 dice, or 100 cubes of wood with one face of each marked
○ container for throwing dice

1 Throw the dice. Remove any that fall with the marked face (or a selected number) uppermost.

2 Record the number of dice removed. Deduce and record the number remaining.

3 Throw the REMAINDER, remove those with the marked face uppermost, and again record the number removed and the number remaining.

4 Repeat step three until there are only about five dice left.

5 Plot a graph of the number of dice remaining against the number of throws.

6 If each throw represents one unit of time, what is the half-life of the decay of the number of dice?

7 Estimate the number of throws that would be needed to eliminate all the dice.

2 Computer simulation

There are a number of computer programs that illustrate the way that radioactive substances decay. The program you use may demonstrate the dice method for plotting a decay curve or produce a decay curve using a large sample of 'radioactive atoms'. Your teacher will give you further instructions depending on the program used.

continued

B Half-life of a radioactive isotope

1 Using a scaler

Safety

Make sure you have read and understood the safety rules in the *Students' resource book* before you start this experiment.

Apparatus

O GM tube
O scaler or ratemeter
O protactinium solution in
O plastic bottle
O stop-clock

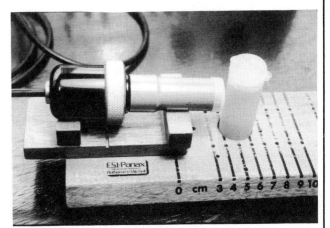

Figure 4.9

1 Set up the apparatus as shown in figure 4.9 but *without* the bottle in place. Set the voltage on the scaler to the operating voltage of the GM tube. Measure and record the background count rate.

2 Shake the protactinium solution vigorously, and place the bottle in front of the GM tube. Make sure the tube is close to the organic layer and start counting immediately the layers of liquid have separated out.

3 Take the count in the following way: start the scaler counting and let it run for 10 seconds; stop for 10 seconds, and record the count reading; start again, and run for another 10 seconds; stop for 10 seconds and record the count. Continue this sequence until the count drops to little more than background level. You thus get 10 seconds count; 10 seconds interval; 10 seconds count;

and so on.

Note. The experiment is easier if two people work together. If you are working on your own, try letting the scaler run on, taking every alternative 10 second interval. (If you are using a ratemeter, set a 5 second integrating time and record the count every 10 seconds until it falls to a little more than background level.)

4 Draw up a table of your results. Plot a graph of corrected count rate (count rate minus background count rate) against time.

5 What effect would the background count have had on the shape of the graph if you had not allowed for it?

6 From your graph, what can you deduce about the way protactinium decayed?

7 What is the half-life of protactinium? Make five estimates from your graph and average them.

continued

EXPERIMENT EN 10

2 Using the VELA

Safety

Make sure you have read and understood the safety rules in the *Students' resource book* before you start this experiment.

Apparatus

○ GM tube
○ Unilab GM tube EHT unit
○ Protactinium solution in plastic bottle
○ VELA

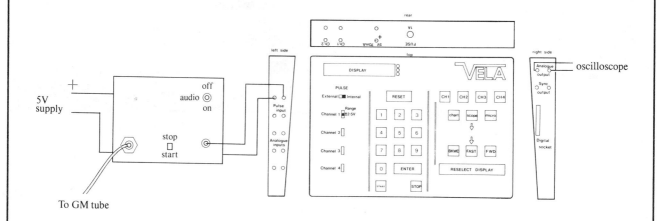

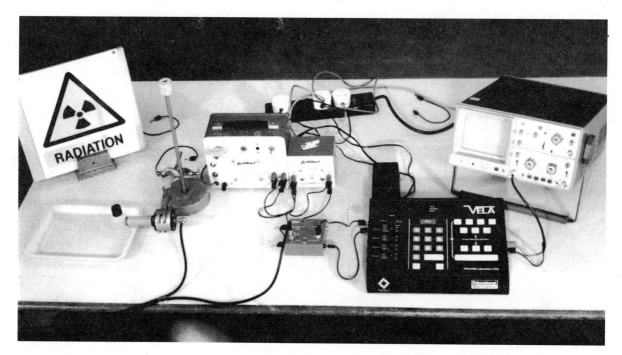

Figure 4.10

continued

EXPERIMENT EN 10

1 Set up the VELA as shown in figure 4.10 (and connect to pulse unit with GM tube lead without the bottle in place). Measure and record the background rate using program 07.

2 Key in the following:

[0] [7] [5] [ENTER] (This sets the time interval to 5 s.)

3 Shake the protactinium solution vigorously and place the bottle in front of the GM tube. Make sure the tube is close to the organic layer and press [START] immediately the layers of liquid have separated out.

4 This display will show the number of the reading being taken and the oscilloscope will show a continuously updated graph. To stop the program, press [STOP]. The oscilloscope display can then be obtained by pressing [CHI] and then [SCOPE].

5 If the necessary equipment is available the data can be downloaded through a computer to a printer for display as a graph.

6 Calculation of the half-life involves subtracting the background count rate from each reading. The reading can be extracted from the VELA by keying in the following: [RESELECT DISPLAY] (arrow) [CHI] (arrow) [SCOPE]. The contents of memory location 1 (the first reading) are displayed. Pressing [FWD] will allow the other readings to be extracted.

7 A graph of net count rate against time can be drawn and the half-life calculated as described in EN 11(c).

EXPERIMENT EN 11

Monitoring radiation

Each of the two experiments will require about 0.5 hour to set up and they can then be left running. The aim of EN 11A, 'Background radiation', is to monitor this radiation over a period of 1 day. With EN 11B, 'Variations in emission rate', the aim is to show that emission rates are never constant and to illustrates the random nature of radioactive decay.

A Background radiation

Apparatus

○ GM tube
○ Unilab GM tube EHT unit
○ VELA
○ Oscilloscope

1 Set up the VELA as shown in figure 4.10 with the GM tube connected to the pulse unit. The action of the Unilab module is to provide 420 V for the operation of the GM tube and to provide suitable rectangular pulses that can be used by the VELA.

2 The program 07 counts pulses over time intervals determined by the user. However, only 255 readings can be taken and the maximum number of pulses counted in the time interval must be less than 255. For long term monitoring of the background radiation, the time interval should obviously be as long as possible To monitor the radiation over 24 hours, the time interval will need to be of the order of 6 minutes. If the number of pulses is close to 255 in this time, the time interval will need to be cut down. A preliminary run will determine this.

3 Key in the following:

　[0] [7] [3] [6] [0] [ENTER] (This sets the time interval
　　　　　　　　　　　　　　　　to 360 s.)
　[START]

4 The display will show which of the readings is being taken. The oscilloscope shows a continually updated graph of the number of pulses counted in the time interval against time. Not much will be seen until the experiment has been running for some time. After the 255 readings have been taken, the full graph is obtained by pressing [CHI] and then [SCOPE].

5 If the necessary equipment is available, the data can be downloaded through a computer to a printer.

B Variations in emission rate

Apparatus

○ GM tube
○ Unilab GM tube EHT unit
○ VELA
○ Radioisotope
○ Oscilloscope

1 It might be expected with a radioisotope of very long half-life (for example, uranium-238 has a half-life of 4.5×10^9 years) that the count rate will not vary during the time interval over which measurements might be made in the laboratory. Using the VELA to store a large number of readings shows that this is not so.

2 Set up the VELA as shown in figure 4.10 with the GM tube connected to the pulse unit. It is important that the number of emissions detected in the time interval used should not exceed 255. A suitable average value would be half this. A preliminary run through using program 07 allows the separation of the source and the GM tube to be varied to achieve this.

3 The program 09 shows the distribution of the count rates. This can be displayed on an oscilloscope. The horizontal axis shows the count rate (from 0 to 255) in the time interval and the vertical axis the number of times that the count rate occurred (from 0 to 255). When the number of times that a particular count rate occurred reaches 255, the program stops.

4 Key in the following:

　[0] [9] [2] [ENTER] (This sets the time interval to 2 s,
　　　　　　　　　　　　but other values can be used.)
　[START]

The display will show the number of the reading being taken and the oscilloscope will show a continually updated graph. To stop the program, press [STOP]. The oscilloscope display can then be obtained by pressing [CHI] and then [SCOPE].

6 If the necessary equipment is available the data can be downloaded through a computer to a printer for display as a graph.

7 From the oscilloscope display or the computer print-out, explain the shape of the observed curve. What value would you suggest for the emission rate?

Questions on objectives

1 The *radioisotope* of sodium, $^{24}_{11}$Na, has a *half-life* of 15 hours, and disintegrates to a *daughter nuclide* with the emission of beta particles and gamma rays.

Explain, in one sentence for each, the meanings of the three terms in italics. *(objective 1)*

2 What type(s) of radiation would you expect to be emitted in the following processes? Explain your answers.
(a) Radium $^{226}_{88}$Ra decays into radon $^{222}_{86}$Rn.
(b) Rubidium $^{87}_{37}$Rb decays into strontium $^{87}_{38}$Sr.

(objective 3)

3 Complete the equations for the radioactive decay process below.

$$^{232}_{90}\text{Th} \rightarrow {}^{228}_{88}\text{Ra} + \text{(a)}$$

$$^{228}_{88}\text{Ra} \rightarrow \text{(b)} + 2{}^{0}_{-1}\text{e}$$

(objective 3)

4 It is a theoretical prediction that electrons are not constituents of nuclei. How can this be reconciled with the observed phenomenon of beta decay? *(objective 4)*

5 Two radioactive sources Q and R initially contain equal numbers of radioactive atoms. Source Q has a half-life of one hour, and source R a half-life of two hours. Calculate the value of the fraction

number of atoms of Q unchanged
number of atoms of R unchanged

after a time of four hours. *(objective 6)*

6 The radioisotope oxygen-15 has a half-life of approximately 2 minutes, and decays by the emission of beta (-) particles.

(a) How many particles would be emitted by a 1 mg sample of the isotope in 6 minutes?
(b) Why can this figure only be approximate?
(N_A = 6.02 x 1023 mol^{-1}) *(objectives 6 and 7)*

7 Choose three of the following radioisotopes and give one use for each of those chosen: cobalt-60, phosphorus-32, carbon-14, uranium-235, iodine -131. *(objective 10)*

8 The law for the decay of a radioactive isotope may be stated as $N = N_0\, e^{-\lambda t}$
(a) Identify the symbols N, N_o and λ .
(b) Explain in words the meaning of the equation.
(objectives 8 and 9)

9 (a) What is the decay constant of radon-220, half-life 55.5 s?
(b) What is the half-life of uranium-238, decay constant 4.87 x 10^{-18} s^{-1}? *(objectives 8 and 9)*

10 What is the number of disintegrations per second of 1.00 mg of uranium-238? *(objectives 8 and 9)*

11 Why is a gram of radium (half-life 1600 years) much more dangerous than a gram of uranium (half-life 4.5 x 10^9 years)? *(objectives 7 and 11)*

12 Explain the different safety precautions appropriate to α, β and γ radiations, with reference to their relevant properties. *(objective 11)*

13 Some of the stonework of the Acropolis in Athens repaired in the nineteenth century, is cracking. How could you check if this is due to the internal rusting of iron bars used to strengthen the stonework? *(objective 10)*

Nuclear physics

Study time: 1.5 weeks

Summary

In this topic you will study the factors which determine the stability of nuclei and develop an hypothesis for predicting how stability will change in different nuclear transformations. You will find out how some nuclear changes result in the liberation of energy and then apply that knowledge to explain how nuclear energy is produced from fission and fusion.

Objectives

When you have completed this topic you should be able to:

1 Use the following words and phrases with their correct scientific meaning: nuclear force, critical size, strong interaction, chain reaction, binding energy, moderation, mass defect, thermal reactor, stable and unstable nuclei, breeder reactor, fusion, fission.

2 Recall the relationship between mass and energy and relate the energy changes occurring in nuclear transformations to the changes in nuclear mass.

3 Recall and describe the relationship between proton number (Z) and neutron number (N) for stable nuclei and use it to predict stability.

4 Recall and describe how the mass defect per nucleon depends on the nucleon number (A) of stable nuclides and relate this to nuclear stability.

5 Describe changes which produce energy from nuclear fusion and fission.

6 Solve problems involving calculations of energy release and mass changes in nuclear transformations.

7 Describe the basic design of nuclear reactors.

Note. All of this topic is only required for certain Boards, much of it is *only* required for options in the JMB and London syllabuses. Check your syllabus and discuss with your teacher how much you should cover.

Experiments

EN 12 Liquid drop model of nuclear fission (0.5 hour)

References

Akrill	Chapter 19
Caro	Chapters 15 and 16
Duncan	Chapter 25
Muncaster	Chapter 53
Nelkon	Chapter 35
Wenham	Chapter 48
Whelan	Chapter 64

5.1 Nuclear stability

In this topic we shall ask:

How can we account for the great stability of some nuclei and the instability of others?
What is the source of the energy released in nuclear transformations and how can it be assessed and utilised?

First, we must try to answer the questions: how densely packed are particles within the nucleus, and what holds the nucleus together?

A compact nucleus

One technique for measuring the size of the nucleus is to observe how high speed particles, particularly electrons, are scattered by nuclei. Figure 5.1 shows how electrons are scattered by an oxygen nucleus. The shape of the graph with its maxima and minima shows that the electrons scattered by the nucleus behave like waves diffracted by an obstacle. From this graph the size of an oxygen nucleus and its density can be calculated.

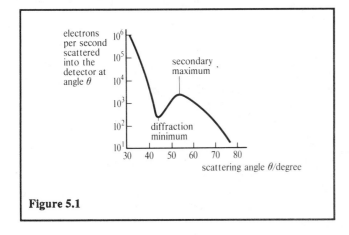

Figure 5.1

Q 5.1 Development question*

The wavelength of an electron depends on its momentum and is given by the equation:

$$\text{wavelength} = \frac{\text{Planck constant}}{\text{electron momentum}}$$

(a) Why do you think it is necessary to use very high speed electrons if diffraction patterns of nuclei are to be observed?

The scattered electrons shown on the graph (figure 5.1) have a momentum which makes them behave like waves of wavelength 3×10^{-15} m.

(b) According to the theory of diffraction of waves by a circular obstacle

$$\sin \theta_1 = \frac{1.22 \, \lambda}{D}$$

where θ_1 is the scattering angle for the first minimum of the graph and D is the diameter of the obstacle (the oxygen nucleus).

Calculate D and hence the volume of the oxygen nucleus (assuming it to be spherical).
(c) Calculate the density of the nucleus of oxygen-16 assuming neutrons and protons each have mass 1.7×10^{-27} kg.
(d) Compare the density of the nucleus of oxygen with the density of water (1000 kg m^{-3}) ∎

The evidence shows a nuclear density of the order of 10^{14} times greater than that of ordinary matter and indicates how dense matter could become if all the matter of atoms were compressed into their nuclei.

Such compressed matter is believed to exist at the high pressure and temperature within some stars. A 5 ml teaspoonful of this kind of matter would have the same mass as a mountain like Ben Nevis. The force needed to hold matter so densely packed within the nucleus cannot be provided by gravitational or electric forces - they are too weak and act over too great a distance. It is necessary to propose another kind of force - the nuclear force or **strong interaction** which holds protons and neutrons powerfully together but which has a short range (not acting beyond 2×10^{-15} m).

Pulling the nucleus apart

Energy will be needed to overcome the effect of this nuclear force to remove a nucleon (proton or neutron) from the nucleus. The work which must be done to dissociate the nucleus into separated nucleons is called the **binding energy** of the nucleus. How can we measure this energy? A clue may be found by looking at nuclear changes which seem to create energy. Look again at the famous experiment of Cockroft and Walton on bombarding lithium with protons (section 3.3). We noted that the α-particles produced had more mechanical energy than was provided by the bombarding proton.

Q 5.2 Self-assessment question

Use the data provided in table 5.1 to calculate the mass of the lithium-7 nucleus. Is mass conserved when α-particles are produced by bombarding lithium with protons? ∎

Table 5.1 Masses of some particles and nuclides*

Symbol name	Mass in atomic mass units/u	Symbol or name	Mass in atomic mass units/u
electron	0.0005	$^{7}_{3}$Li	7.0160
proton	1.0073	$^{12}_{6}$C	12.000
neutron	1.0087	$^{14}_{7}$N	14.0031
$^{1}_{1}$H	1.0078	$^{16}_{8}$O	15.9949
$^{2}_{1}$H	2.0141	$^{17}_{8}$O	16.9991
$^{3}_{2}$He	3.0160	$^{18}_{8}$O	17.9991
$^{4}_{2}$He	4.0026		
α-particle	4.0015		

*The data given for complete atoms is that of a neutral atom including its electrons. 1 u = 1.66 x 10^{-27} kg.

This nuclear change produces a change in mass. This is a strange result but such a possibility had been predicted by Einstein in 1905, 25 years before Cockroft and Walton's experiment. In his Special Theory of Relativity he postulated that the mass m of a particle moving at speed v relative to an observer would be measured by him to be

$$m = \frac{m_0}{\sqrt{(1 - v^2/c^2)}}$$

where m_o is its rest mass. A result of this theory is an equivalence of mass and energy and a conservation of mass-energy in every process. His theory predicts that a body gaining energy ΔE thereby increases its mass by an amount Δm given by

$$\Delta E = c^2 \, \Delta m$$

(or, if you prefer, the world's most famous equation $E = mc^2$) where c is the speed of light. The conservation of mass-energy can be expressed in balancing equations in which mass and energy are summed up on both sides.

It should be noted that this equation does not refer to the *conversion* of mass into energy or vice versa, as commonly stated. Mass and energy are always co-existent. The equation can be used to find how much of either there is in a situation at a particular time.

There is a mass decrease when two α-particles are produced by proton bombardment of lithium-7 because energy has been released.

Q 5.3 Self-assessment question

How much energy release results from a mass decrease of 1 gram? ■

Your answer is an amount of energy which will drive a large car 100 times around the world - energy long outlasting the car!

All energy changes also involve mass changes but in most everyday processes the quantities of energy are too small to produce detectable changes in mass.

Q 5.4 Self-assessment question

(a) What increase in mass is predicted by Einstein's equation when 1 kg of water is heated from 0°C to 100°C?
(s.h.c. water = 4200 J K^{-1} kg^{-1})
(b) What is the order of magnitude of the energy change per molecule as a result of this heating?
(Molar mass of water = 18 g) ■

In nuclear changes, the quantities of energy involved are of the order of 10^{-13} J per atom and produce significant changes in the masses of the particles involved. A convenient unit for measuring these energy changes is 1 MeV.
(1 MeV = 1.6 x 10^{-13} J.)

Q 5.5 Self-assessment question

(a) What is the mass equivalent of 1.0 MeV of energy? How does this mass compare with the rest mass of an electron? (m_e = 9.1 x 10^{-31} kg)
(b) What is the mass of a 1 MeV β-particle? ■

Thus, the emission of a 1 MeV β–particle will carry away from the nucleus a mass about three times the rest mass of the electron.

Q 5.6 Self-assessment question

(a) When α-particles bombard nitrogen (see Rutherford's experiment, section 2.4) what is the change in mass produced (in atomic mass units)?
(b) Is more energy liberated than is supplied?

Explain your answer and calculate the energy change in MeV. (A mass change of 1 u produces an energy change of 931 MeV.)

(c) What makes the reaction possible?
(d) The α-particles from radium have an energy of 7.7 MeV. How much energy is shared by the proton and $^{17}_{8}O$ nucleus? ■

Binding energy and mass defect

Mass changes occur when a lithium nucleus splits into two α-particles and you can now find out if there are any mass changes involved in *building up a nucleus* from its component particles.

Q 5.7 Self-assessment question

Use the data in table 5.1 to calculate any mass changes that are produced by the building up of
(a) a nucleus of deuterium,
(b) an α-particle. ■

Both deuterium and helium nuclei have a mass which is less than the sum of the masses of their component nucleons - a **mass defect**. Mass shortage is demonstrative of lost energy. We can infer that nuclear mass defect is the measure of the energy given out when the nucleus was first formed. This energy is the binding energy of the nucleus.

Q 5.8 Self-assessment question

Calculate the binding energy of an α-particle in MeV. ■

Stable nuclei

If there is a strong attractive force between neutrons and protons within the nucleus, is it possible for neutrons and protons to come together in any number to form an infinite variety of nuclei? The answer is clearly no! There are a very limited number of stable nuclei although scientists are constantly producing more unstable nuclei. Figure 5.2 shows all stable nuclei (each represented by a black dot) on a graph of N (neutron number) against Z (proton number).

Q 5.9 Self-assessment question

(a) Does the graph agree with the data in table 5.1 for O, Cl and Sn?
(b) For nuclei with Z less than 20, what is the relationship between Z and N?

(c) What happens to the ratio N:Z for larger nuclei?

(d) Which nuclei have the largest neutron excess?

(e) Only two stable nuclei are indicated in figure 5.2 with a proton excess. Which nuclei are these? ■

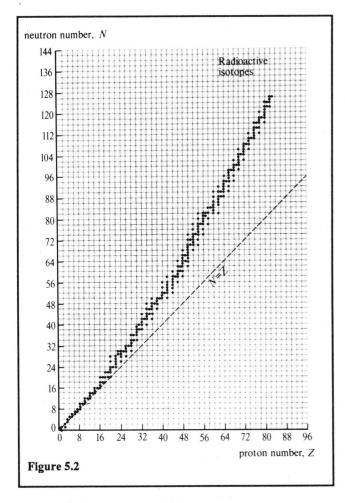

Figure 5.2

The stability of a nucleus will depend on the competition between the attractive nuclear force (between neutrons and protons) and the repulsive electrical force (between protons). The nuclear force appears to favour the binding of pairs of particles and pairs of pairs (a pair of protons and a pair of neutrons). Thus, the α-particle is a very stable nucleus and only four stable nuclei have both odd Z and odd N: ^2_1H, ^6_3Li, $^{10}_5B$ and $^{14}_7N$.

In the absence of electrical interactions, the most stable nuclei would be those that have N = Z. The electrical force shifts the balance in favour of a greater number of neutrons but a nucleus with too many neutrons is unstable (because not enough neutrons are paired with protons).

The curve in figure 5.2 doesn't go on for ever. Though *unstable* nuclides have been observed with Z as large as 112, it was thought until recently that the largest stable nuclei have Z = 83. In recent years, however, there have been suggestions that there may be larger nuclei, so-called 'super-heavy stable elements'.

Binding energy per nucleon

How can we compare the stability of different nuclides?

Are all nuclei equally stable? Are isotopes of the same element equally stable? The mass spectrometer provides

answers to these questions by enabling us to calculate the mass defect and binding energy of every nuclide. The graph (figure 5.3) shows binding energy per nucleon plotted against nucleon number.

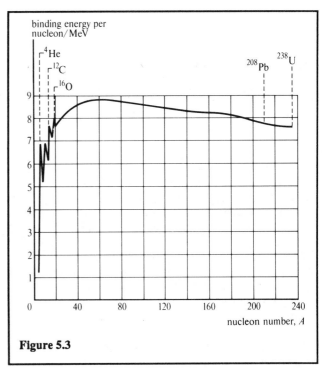

Figure 5.3

Notice that:

1 The graph shows that binding energy per nucleon is a maximum for iron (A = 56) one of the most stable nuclides;

2 ^4_2He, $^{16}_8O$, $^{12}_6C$ have relatively high binding energy per nucleon amongst the lighter nuclides (see peaks in figure 5.3) and these are the most stable light nuclei;

3 For more massive nuclei (A > 60) the binding energy per nucleon decreases as A increases.

Q 5.10 Self-assessment question

Does the graph agree with your own calculation (in question 5.8) of binding energy for helium? ■

For a particular value of A (nucleon number) there must be one particular value of Z (proton number) which produces the greatest mass defect and most stable nuclide. These stable nuclides constitute the most common elements in the universe - the more stable, the more abundant. In the universe, H and He are the most abundant; in the earth's crust, O and Si; in the earth's interior, we presume Fe most abundant. For light elements Z for stable nuclei is approximately 1/2A (see figure 5.2).

Q 5.11 Self-assessment question

(a) The atomic masses of the three stable isotopes of oxygen are given in table 5.1. Calculate the mass defect and binding energy per nucleon for each isotope. (1 u of mass is equivalent to 931 MeV of energy.)

(b) Does your answer agree with the data in figure 5.3 for $^{16}_{8}O$?
(c) How do your results correlate with the relative abundance of these isotopes given in table 5.1? ∎

Radioactive decay

Each dot in figure 5.2 represents a stable nuclide. Unstable nuclides will be located above or below the plot of dots for stable nuclides.

Naturally occurring radioactive nuclides are located in the region shown in figure 5.2. They have a greater value of the ratio N/Z than stable nuclides. They will decay to a stable nuclide by emitting radioactive particles, thus changing the values of N and Z. A move towards stability for these nuclides involves a decrease in the ratio N/Z.

There are also unstable isotopes of lighter elements which have a surplus of protons and tend to move in the opposite direction in the graph by a decay process. Consider the changes occurring when different types of radiation are emitted.

Beta decay may involve the emission of β^--particles or β^+-particles.

Q 5.12 Self-assessment question

(a) What happens to the value of Z, the value of N, and the ratio N/Z when a nuclide emits a β^--particle.
(b) In which direction will the change move the nuclide on the graph of N against Z?
(c) In which region of the graph are unstable nuclides located which emit (i) β^--particles, (ii) β^+-particles? ∎

α-decay produces an increase of nuclear stability as a heavy nucleus like uranium-238 ejects a very stable lump of matter (a helium nucleus) and is transformed into a lighter nucleus (α–thorium-234). The change results in a move along the binding energy curve (figure 5.3) towards the maximum stability region. Notice from the curve that the total binding energy of the two products (α and thorium) is greater than the original binding energy of the uranium. Since binding energy and mass defect have both increased, the total mass of the product is less than the original and this loss of mass results in energy released as 4.2 MeV of kinetic energy, mostly for the emitted α-particle.

Q 5.13 Self-assessment question

Write down the equation of the decay of uranium-238 into thorium-234. ∎

Most naturally-occurring radioactive nuclides belong to one of three possible decay series. Each series begins with a radioactive nuclide of very long half-life (^{238}U, ^{235}U or ^{232}Th) of about 10^9 years. These nuclides decay to produce a series of radioactive products with half-lives varying from thousands of years to less than a millionth of a second. Each series ends with the production of a stable isotope of lead.

Q 5.14 Self-assessment question

Thorium ($^{228}_{90}Th$) is an isotope in a radioactive series which decays with the successive emission of: α, α, α, α, β^-, β^-, α.
(a) Find the value of Z and A for the final product.
(b) Suggest a reason why a series of α emissions is likely to be followed by one or more β emissions. ∎

Gamma emission

When a nuclear transformation produces a loss of mass there is an accompanying energy release. This energy will appear as the kinetic energy of ejected particles some may also be emitted as a quantum of γ radiation. Hence, γ radiation often accompanies α and β emission though sometimes γ radiation is emitted on its own.

EXTENSION

Beta and gamma emissions also provide clues about the nature of the nucleus and these are considered in this extension.

Q 5.15 Study question

(a) What explanations have been suggested for the fact that γ rays are sometimes emitted without any other simultaneous radiations?
(b) What evidence is there of the existence of energy levels within the nucleus? ∎

Q 5.16 Study question

Beta particles emitted during nuclear transformations have energies which are distributed throughout a wide spectrum. Find out how the neutrino hypothesis attempts to explain this continuous beta spectrum. ∎

5.2 Nuclear fission

Our study of stability of nuclei in the last section indicated that:
1 Stability depends entirely on the ratio of neutrons to protons in a nucleus.
2 Very massive nuclei, like uranium, are less stable than medium-sized nuclei, like iron.

The increase in the number of excess neutrons in a massive nucleus seems an obvious way to produce an unstable element. In the 1930s, several scientists used slow neutrons to bombard uranium. In 1939, two German scientists made a dramatic discovery that this neutron bombardment produced not only a lot of energy but the products of the change included barium and krypton - elements which are much lighter than uranium. The explanation for this was that an isotope of uranium (uranium-235) had captured a neutron, become unstable and broken into pieces. This break up of a large nucleus is called **fission**.

Q 5.17 Self-assessment question

Complete the equation representing a possible fission reaction

$$^{235}_{92}U + ^{1}_{0}n \longrightarrow ? \longrightarrow ^{141}_{56}Ba + ^{92}_{36}Kr + ? + energy \blacksquare$$

Fission of uranium-235 does not always produce this particular change but always two large lumps of matter and several neutrons are produced (on average 2.5 neutrons per fission).

A good model to help visualise the fission process is provided by creating instability in a liquid drop which leads eventually to its break up, as illustrated in figure 5.4.

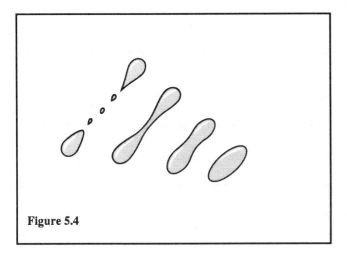

Figure 5.4

E Experiment EN 12
Liquid drop model of nuclear fission

In this experiment you will be able to visualise the fission process by experimenting with a liquid drop.

The experiment can easily be done at home.

Chain reaction

The fission reaction will continue to repeat itself if the fission produces a neutron which itself is captured to produce a further fission. Then a chain of reactions will be set up and the process will just keep going without any help from outside. If each fission of uranium-235 produces three neutrons, each of which produces further fission, then the chain reaction has a reproduction factor of three and produces an ever-increasing, uncontrolled and catastrophic energy release.

How does our world survive for millions of years with great lumps of uranium ore in the rocks? Why doesn't a chain reaction occur? Fortunately for us, naturally-occurring uranium contains only 0.7% of fissile uranium-235 and more than 99% of uranium-238, an isotope which captures neutrons without breaking up, and so no chain reaction occurs.

In the next question you will find out whether it is possible to have a safe piece of pure uranium-235.

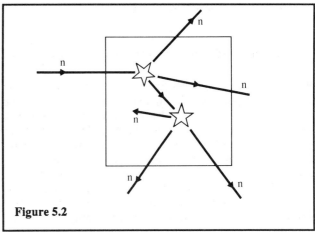

Figure 5.2

Q 5.18 Self-assessment question

Figure 5.5 shows a piece of uranium-235 bombarded by a neutron which produces fission. Two of the product neutrons have travelled through the block of uranium without being captured and so escape, but one of the product neutrons has produced a new fission.

(a) What is the reproduction factor in this case? Is a chain reaction possible if this average reproduction is maintained?
(b) Would a chain reaction be possible in a smaller piece of uranium-235? Explain your answer.
(c) What would happen if the piece of uranium-235 was larger than in figure 5.5?
(d) Suggest a definition of **critical mass**. ■

The first atomic bomb (more correctly described as a nuclear bomb) used two pieces of uranium-235 below the critical mass and kept apart. To trigger the nuclear explosion they were brought together very quickly and a chain reaction resulted, released vast energy in a very short time interval and a temperature of millions of degrees. Apart from the blast, beta particles, neutrons, protons and gamma rays were emitted. In the nuclear explosion which destroyed Hiroshima, 70 000 people were killed by the immediate blast and many more died from radiation effects. All this horror as a result of a mass loss of 0.23 g.

Fission and superstition
(A cautionary verse for parents or children appropriate to the Christmas season.)

This is the tale of Frederick Wermyss
Whose parents weren't on speaking terms.
So when Fred wrote to Santa Claus
It was in duplicate because
One went to Dad and one to Mum -
Both asked for some Plutonium.
See the result: Father and Mother
Without consulting one another
Purchased two lumps of largish size
Intending them as a surprise
Which met in Frederick's stocking and
Laid level ten square miles of land.

MORAL

Learn from this dismal tale of fission
Not to mix Science with Superstition.
(H.M.K. *New Statesman & Nation*, 14.1.1950)

A controlled chain reaction - the atomic pile

Whether a fission process grows into a chain reaction or fizzles out depends on the reproduction factor just as this factor affects the world population. An average of 5 children per family will lead to an increasing rate of population growth (uncontrolled chain reaction) whilst two children per family or less will result in a steady decline in population and eventual extinction. Static population requires about 2.3 children on average per family. Controlled and steady energy release from fission requires that for each fission of uranium-235 by the capture of a neutron, only one product neutron produces further fission, the other neutrons escaping or being absorbed - a reproduction factor of one.

The first controlled chain reaction was produced by Fermi in 1942 using uranium. He used cadmium rods to capture surplus neutrons and so keep the reproduction factor down to 1.0006. The absorbing cadmium rods are called **control rods**. Boron is often used to absorb surplus neutrons.

The first atomic pile only produced enough energy to light two 100 W lamps but it established the possibility of nuclear reactors.

The reproduction factor also depends on the speed of the neutrons which determines their chance of being captured and producing more fission. If neutrons travel too fast, there is less chance of their being captured to produce fission. If the neutrons can be slowed down, the chances of fission occurring will increase and the reproduction factor will increase. A substance which is used to slow down neutrons is called a **moderator**; graphite (carbon) is often used.

Uranium-238 captures slow and medium speed neutrons and the resulting nucleus decays in two stages of β emission to produce plutonium ($^{239}_{94}$Pu). Plutonium-239 is relatively stable (half-life 25 000 years) but what is much more important, it can undergo fission by slow neutrons. So, if uranium-238 is used as a fuel for a reaction, a new fuel is produced by the reactor: it is called a breeder reactor.

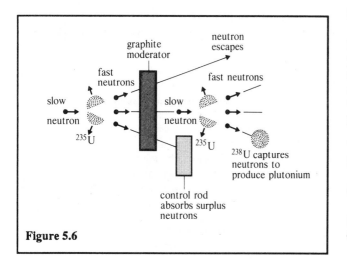

Figure 5.6

Figure 5.6 illustrates the various processes which occur in a uranium reactor.

Q 5.19 Study question

Describe briefly how the various components shown in figure 5.6 are used in the construction of a simple nuclear pile. Sketch the construction and mention any other materials used. ■

Q 5.20 Self-assessment question

(a) What is the function of the moderator?
(b) What happens to the energy of a fast neutron as it is slowed down by the moderator?
(c) Suggest why a material like $^{12}_{6}$C makes a good moderator.
(d) In a nuclear pile using boron control rods, the following reaction occurs

$$^{10}_{5}\text{B}(^{1}_{0}\text{n}, ^{4}_{2}\alpha)^{7}_{3}\text{Li}$$

How does this expression indicate that boron is good material for the control rods?

(e) What is the effect of pushing the control rods into the pile? Why is it necessary to pull the control rods out very slowly over a period of hours or days? ■

Q 5.21 Self-assessment question

Explain the process which enables an atomic pile to breed new fissile fuel. Include the equation of the reaction in your answer. ■

Q 5.22 Study/Discussion question*

Britain's present nuclear power stations are mainly Magnox type, with a few Advanced Gas Cooled types. The new design is the Pressurised Water Reactor. What are the differences between the three types in respect of their fuel, moderator and coolant? What are the advantages and disadvantages of each type? ■

Further information, references and questions on this topic will be found in the topic options *Energy and its uses* and *Nuclear physics*.

5.3 Energy from fusion

Look again at figure 5.3. You should recall that a fission process which liberates energy involves moving from the extreme right of the curve, uphill towards iron-56, as a large uranium nucleus is broken up. Where else on the curve would it be possible to move up the slope? What kind of process would achieve this uphill movement in the graph?

Your answer will suggest that a fusion of two light nuclei like hydrogen or deuterium would produce an energy release.

Q 5.23 Self-assessment question

(a) Write down the equation representing the fusion of two deuterium nuclei to produce $^{3}_{2}$He.

(b) Calculate the mass change (in kg) and energy released (in J) for each fusion reaction. Hence, find the energy released by the fusion of 1 kg of deuterium. (See table 5.1 for data.)

Thermonuclear reactions

Because of the mutual electrostatic repulsion of nuclear charges it is difficult to push two protons or two deuterium nuclei together. Only nuclei with very large kinetic energies can overcome the repelling electric forces and undergo fusion. One way of achieving this would be to accelerate one or both particles in a machine.

Q 5.24 Self-assessment question

How else can nuclei be given very high energy? ∎

Fusion of two nuclei can occur at extremely high temperatures (2×10^7 K or higher) and so these reactions are called thermonuclear reactions. Once started, the energy release of the thermonuclear reaction maintains the high temperature and keeps the reaction going. The problem is in starting it, and the only man-produced thermonuclear reaction (a hydrogen bomb) was initiated by producing uncontrolled fission of uranium.

It is fusion of hydrogen into helium which provides the main energy source within the sun and stars at temperatures of millions of kelvin.

Q 5.25 Self-assessment question

Figure 5.7 shows the three stages of a thermonuclear reaction taking place in the sun involving the fusion of protons.

(a) At stage (1) four protons combine to produce two nuclei of deuterium and two particles are emitted. What is each particle X?
(b) At stage (2) a proton is captured by each deuterium nucleus. What are nuclei Y?
(c) At stage (3) two nuclei Y undergo fusion. What are particles Z?
(d) What is the net change as a result of all these stages? ∎

The fusion process illustrated in figure 5.7 produces no harmful radiation products but provides 26 MeV of energy from the fusion of four protons.

It is estimated that the sun is losing 4×10^9 kg of mass every second in this way but, don't worry, it is expected to carry on doing this for 10^{10} years!

Scientists are now attempting to produce the high temperature which would make possible controlled fusion reactions. Machines called **tokomaks** have already been developed to produce temperatures of more than 1 million kelvin - at least for a brief moment! Even for short periods the high temperature matter (called **plasma**) cannot be contained in material containers but must be held in plasma bottles which use the forces of magnetic fields to contain the plasma (figure 5.8). If such high temperatures could be maintained, the fusion of light elements could take place in controlled conditions and Mankind would have an almost limitless energy source. The estimated mass of the oceans is 10^{21} kg so there is enough deuterium in the sea to provide power for ten thousand million years!

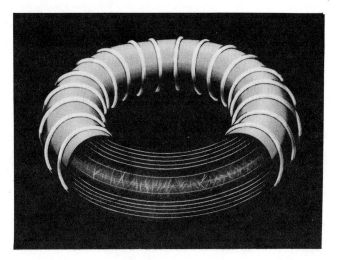

Figure 5.8

Q 5.26 Discussion question

"Though there is much international competition in fusion research, especially between the big tokamaks to be the first to achieve breakeven, there is also much cooperation. Japan's closest cooperation has been with the US. A programme of collaboration began in 1979 as the result of an agreement between President Carter and Prime Minister Fukuda. (Cooperation between Japan and the Soviet Union was due to start the same year, but fizzled out when the Soviet Union invaded Afghanistan.)

Along with the US, the Soviet Union and Europe, Japan also participates in the INTOR (International Tokamak Reactor) workshop. Organised by the International Atomic Energy Agency (IAEA) of the United Nations, INTOR's original purpose was to design and build a fusion reactor based on the tokamak configuration. It has now become clear that the IAEA is unlikely to build such a machine. A scientist who has served as the workshop's chairman since it was established in 1979, says that INTOR still serves a useful purpose because it provides a forum where fusion engineers can discuss and crystallise ideas.

International links between fusion researchers are increasing. Last January, Japan signed a cooperative agreement

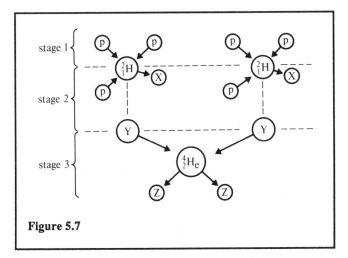

Figure 5.7

with the US and Europe. The agreement, which was sponsored by the International Energy Agency of the OECD, calls for the people working on the three large tokamaks to pool their results''.

New Scientist, 25th February, 1987.

(a) How would you set about finding out what the various acronyms stand for, e.g. INTOR, OECD, etc. (You are not required to actually find out.)
(b) What are the advantages and disadvantages of international cooperation in science in this way? ■

C Comprehension EN 3
What is thermonuclear fusion?

A review of the conditions which must be satisfied to tap nuclear fusion as an energy source.

Liquid drop model of nuclear fission

Apparatus

○ large plate 20 cm diameter
○ light machine oil, e.g. '3 in 1'
○ dripping tap

Procedure

1 Oil the surface of the plate lightly. Place it horizontally under a gently dripping tap and move it slowly about as drops fall on the oiled surface, so that each drop is separate. When you have four or five drops, about the size of a blouse or shirt button on the plate, turn off the tap and examine their behaviour.

2 Tilt the plate so that the drops move. Do they distort very much as they slide slowly across? Do they break up? If you have used the right amount of oil they should slide with little distortion and without breaking up. What happens if two drops meet?

3 Put the plate back under the tap and let several drops fall in the same place. Tilt the plate again and see what happens. Does the larger drop tend to elongate? When it is stretched out long and thin, tilt the plate over to try and make it slide sideways. Does it now break into pieces? Are those pieces usually of unequal size? Are there usually two largish pieces and often a few very small ones?

Questions

1 Water drops hold together because of a short-range force between the molecules (cohesion). What hold the nuclei together in the nucleus?

2 This force generates the 'surface energy', which will always tend to a minimum value for stability. This involves keeping the boundary of the drop as compact as possible. Explain your observations of the large drop splitting up, and the small drops coalescing, in terms of surface energy.

Questions on objectives

1 Explain the terms 'mass defect' and 'binding energy'.
(objective 1)

2 A thoron nucleus ($A = 220$, $Z = 86$) decays with the emission of an α-particle with energy 1.0×10^{-12} J. Write down the values of A and Z for the resulting nucleus.
Calculate the speed of the emitted α-particle and hence deduce the speed of recoil of the product nucleus. (Mass of thoron nucleus is 3.5×10^{-25} kg, mass of particle is 6.7×10^{-27} kg.)
(objectives 2 and 6)

3 $^{226}_{88}$Ra is a nuclide in a radioactive series and decays with the following sequence of emissions: α, α, β, α, β, α. Plot this part of the radioactive series on a graph of neutron number (N) against proton number (Z).

(a) What is the total change in N and Z during the emissions?
(b) Give the value of Z for any nuclides produced. What are the values of A for these nuclides?
(c) How does the ratio $N:Z$ vary for stable nuclei throughout the periodic table?
(d) Discuss the importance of this variation in $N:Z$ to (i) the interspersing of β^- emissions with β^+ emissions in a decay series, and (ii) why β^+ emissions are unlikely.
(objectives 3 and 4)

4 Sketch a graph showing the variation of binding energy per nucleon with nucleon number and show how fusion and fission can be explained from the shape.
(objectives 4 and 5)

The photoelectric effect

Summary

A study of the effect of electromagnetic radiation on matter has profound implications for our understanding of the nature of both. In this topic we will consider the pioneering theory of Einstein, and its experimental support from Millikan.

The photograph shows Albert Einstein at the time of his pioneering work into the nature of the photoelectric effect.

Objectives

When you have completed the work in this topic you should be able to:

1 Use the following scientific terms correctly: photon, threshold frequency, the Planck constant, quantum.

2 Explain what is meant by the photoelectric effect.

3 Describe an experiment to demonstrate the emission of photoelectrons.

4 State how the rate of emission of photoelectrons and their energy depends upon the intensity and frequency of the incident radiation.

5 Give an expression for the energy of a photon, and state the meaning of the symbols and units involved.

6 State the basic principle of the quantum theory.

7 Explain how the observations of the photoelectric effect (a) were in conflict with the wave theory of electromagnetic radiation,
(b) support the quantum theory of electromagnetic radiation.

8 Explain Einstein's equation for the emission of photoelectrons from a metal.

9 Describe and explain an experiment to verify Einstein's photoelectric equation, to determine the Planck constant, measure the work function of a metal and the maximum kinetic energy of the emitted electrons.

10 Solve problems involving the energy of a photon and Einstein's photoelectric equation.

11 Describe at least two practical applications of photocells.

Experiments

EN 13 Investigation with a simple photoelectric cell
(0.5 hour)

References

Akrill	Chapter 18
Caro	Chapter 3
Duncan	Chapter 22
Muncaster	Chapter 47
Nelkon	Chapter 34
Wenham	Chapter 44
Whelan	Chapter 62

6.1 The experimental evidence

In this topic you are going to investigate what happens when ultraviolet and light waves are incident on a metallic surface, develop a theory to explain the phenomena and consider some of the practical applications.

The photoelectric effect is an important landmark in the development of ideas and concepts in physics. The results of experiments were in conflict with Maxwell's wave theory of electromagnetic radiation and gave support to the quantum theory which had been introduced in 1900 by Planck to explain the facts of black body radiation.

In your study of electricity and magnetism you will have learned that all electromagnetic waves are periodic changes in electric and magnetic fields which travel through a vacuum with the same speed, i.e. 3.0×10^8 m s^{-1}. When an electromagnetic wave falls on a metal surface it will cause the electrons to oscillate because the wave consists of an oscillating electric field. The detection of radio waves by an aerial shows that the electromagnetic wave can influence the motion of electrons in a metal. We must ask: is it possible for the electrons to gain sufficient energy from the electromagnetic radiation to leave the surface of the metal?

In 1888 it was discovered that this happened when a zinc plate was irradiated by ultraviolet light. The release of electrons from a metallic surface when electromagnetic radiation falls on it is called **photoelectric emission**. The electrons which are released are referred to as **photoelectrons** and the process is called the **photoelectric effect**. The photoelectric effect may be demonstrated using the apparatus shown in figure 6.1. You should read through the stages of the experiment and then answer the questions.

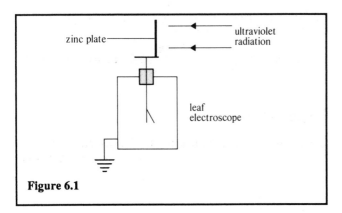

Figure 6.1

In figure 6.2a, a zinc plate (the surface of which has been thoroughly cleaned) is attached to an electroscope and is given a *negative charge*. When radiation from an ultraviolet source, e.g. a mercury vapour lamp, falls on the zinc plate, the leaf of the electroscope falls (figure 6.2b).
In figure 6.2c, the zinc plate is given a *positive* charge and the leaf is deflected. When the ultraviolet source again illuminates the plate, *nothing happens*, the leaf remains deflected (figure 6.2d).

C Computer program
The photoelectric effect

This is a computer simulation of the experiment described below.

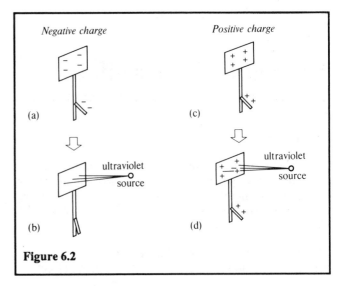

Figure 6.2

Q 6.1 Development question*

(a) Give an explanation for the following observations: (i) the leaf falls when the plate is negatively charged, (ii) the leaf remains deflected when the plate is positively charged.
(b) In figure 6.2b, if a sheet of glass is placed between the source and the zinc plate the leaf remains deflected. Can you suggest a reason for this. ■

The demonstration of the photoelectric effect shows that **negative charge** is released from the zinc plate. Further experiments confirm that the negative charge is due to the release of electrons identical to electrons released from a hot filament.

E Experiment EN 13
Investigation with a simple photoelectric cell

The aim of this experiment is to enable you to make observations and some simple deductions about the photoelectric effect.

Q 6.2 Study question*

(a) What determines whether or not electrons are emitted when the radiation falls on the metal?
(b) What determines the number of photoelectrons that are emitted per second?
(c) How does the maximum speed of emission of the photoelectrons depend upon the frequency of the radiation?
(d) What is the name given to the frequency below which no emission occurs? ■

Photocells
The photoemissive cell

It is found that most metals will emit photoelectrons when illuminated by ultraviolet radiation of a suitable frequency. Some metals, e.g. lithium, sodium, potassium and caesium, will emit electrons under the action of visible light. Caesium is frequently used in photoemissive cells (figure 6.3) which are incorporated into burglar alarm systems, and the sound heads of film projectors.

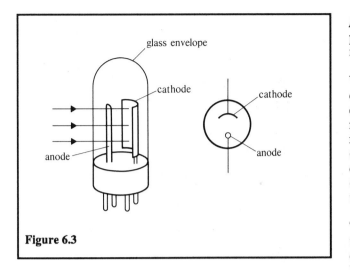

Figure 6.3

The photoconductive cell or light dependent resistor

The resistance of some semiconducting materials such as cadmium sulphide decreases as the intensity of light falls on them. The photons release electrons within the semiconductor, thus increasing conductance. A typical light dependent resistor is shown in figure 6.4.

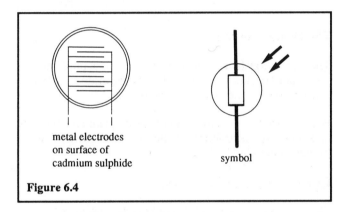

metal electrodes
on surface of
cadmium sulphide

symbol

Figure 6.4

Q 6.3 Study question

(a) Describe the construction and principle of action of a photoemissive cell and light dependent resistor.
(b) Describe two uses of these devices. ■

6.2 Einstein's photoelectric equation

The important experimental fact that electrons will not be released by radiation of less than a certain frequency, regardless of the intensity of the radiation, presented the scientists of the day with a situation that caused them to rethink their ideas on the nature of light and matter. Can this fact be explained by the wave theory?

Q 6.4 Development question*

A certain metal emits electrons when irradiated by blue light but no electrons are emitted when it is irradiated by red light of the same amplitude.
(a) Explain why this observation is in conflict with the electromagnetic theory of radiation.

Note. This theory states that the intensity of the radiation is proportional to the wave amplitude squared. The intensity measures the energy per unit area per second.

When the intensity of the radiation is increased, the number of electrons emitted when irradiated by blue light is increased, but the maximum velocity of the emitted electrons remains the same; the red light does not cause electrons to be released.
(b) Explain why, on the basis of the wave theory, you would expect the maximum speed of the electrons to increase.
(c) What experimental fact can be explained by the wave theory? ■

The electromagnetic wave theory of radiation *cannot* explain the photoelectric effect. A theory *must be able* to account for observed experimental facts. Is then the wave theory wrong? Does it, perhaps, need modifying in order to account for these facts? In 1905, Einstein put forward an explanation that appeared to reject the wave theory. He extended the quantum theory which had been developed by Planck in order to explain black body radiation (considered in the unit *Thermal properties*.)

Planck assumed that radiation is emitted in a whole number of packets or quanta of energy. The energy E of a quantum of radiation of frequency f is given by

$$E = hf$$

where h is a constant, known as the Planck constant.

Einstein assumed that electromagnetic radiation was not only emitted in integral multiples of quanta but that it was also absorbed as quanta or photons. When a photon is absorbed it gives up its energy to a single electron.

Q 6.5 Development question*

Suppose you again consider the experimental fact that a certain metal emits electrons when irradiated by blue light but not by red light (figure 6.5).

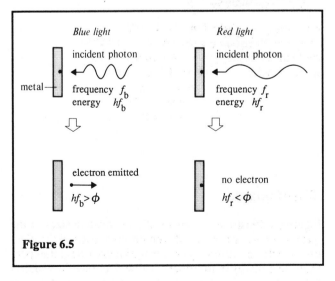

Figure 6.5

(a) How does Einstein's extension of the quantum theory explain the fact that electrons are released from the surface by blue light but not by red light?

Note. In order to liberate an electron from the surface of a metal, a definite minimum amount of energy is required; this is the work function φ of the metal.

(b) What would you expect to happen if the intensity of the blue light, i.e. the number of photons arriving per unit area per unit time, was increased?

(c) Explain why, when green light of a cerain frequency falls on the metal surface, electrons are only just liberated from the surface, i.e. they have no excess energy.
When the metal surface is irradiated by ultraviolet, the maximum speed of the emission electrons is increased. Give an explanation of this fact.■

According to Einstein, an electron may be released from the surface of a metal if the energy of the photon is greater than the work function φ.

That is $hf > \phi$

The excess energy may appear as the kinetic energy of the electron.

Q 6.6 Self-assessment question

(a) Explain the meaning of the Einstein photoelectric equation which may be expressed as

$$hf = e\phi + \tfrac{1}{2}m_e v_{max}^2$$

(b) Suggest why the photoelectrons have a range of speeds up to a maximum value.

(c) If f_o is the frequency of the incident radiation below which no electrons are emitted, i.e. the **threshold frequency**, show that

$$h(f - f_0) = \tfrac{1}{2}m_e v_{max}^2 \quad ■$$

Q 6.7 Self-assessment question

Calculate the maximum kinetic energy with which an electron leaves a caesium surface when exposed to light of wavelength 560 nm.

work function of caesium   = 1.9 eV
charge of electron   = -1.6 x 10⁻¹⁹ C
the Planck constant   = 6.6 x 10⁻³⁴ J s
speed of light   = 3.0 x 10⁸ m s⁻¹ ■

Size of quanta

Figure 6.6 illustrates schematically the relative sizes of the quanta of energy associated with different parts of the electromagnetic spectrum. Quanta in the visible part of the spectrum have energy of the order of a few electronvolts which is sufficient to excite atoms. Gamma rays, in contrast, have a very high frequency and a photon of gamma radiation has an energy of millions of electronvolts. The absorption of a quantum of gamma radiation can change an inheritance gene in a living cell.

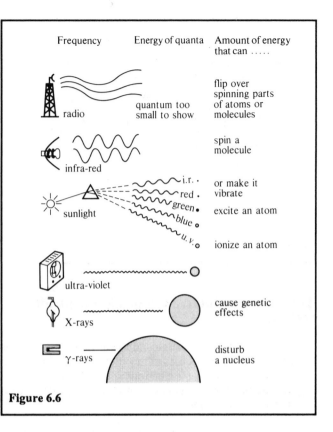

Figure 6.6

The Planck constant

The Planck constant is one of the fundamental physical constants and it occurs in a variety of formulae in atomic physics. The accepted value is $h = 6.63 \times 10^{-34}$ J s.

Because h has an extremely small value, quantum effects are apparent only when we are dealing with small energy changes produced in individual atoms.

Q 6.8 Self-assessment question

Show that the dimensions of the Planck constant are $[M\ L^2\ T^{-1}]$. ■

Q 6.9 Self-assessment question

(a) The BBC Radio 2 transmitter at Droitwich transmits on a wavelength of 1500 m at a power of 400 kW. Calculate the frequency of the radio waves, the energy of one photon of this radiation and the number of photons emitted per second.

(b) A 200 W sodium lamp emits yellow light of wavelength 590 nm. Calculate the energy of one photon of this radiation and the number of photons emitted per second, assuming the lamp is only 25% efficient in converting electrical power to light. (Assume h and c.) ■

Background reference

Gamow, G. *Mr. Tomkins in paperback.* C.U.P, 1965. In this book, Gamow attempts to explain the theory of relativity and the quantum theory by exaggerating existing relativistic phenomena and the magnitude of the Planck constant to such an extent that their effects could be easily observed by the hero of the story, C.G.H. Tomkins, a bank clerk interested in modern science.

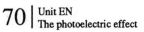

6.3 Millikan's photoelectric experiment

A satisfactory explanation of the photoelectric effect is possible only if it is accepted that light energy is absorbed as photons; the wave theory cannot provide an adequate explanation. Experimental evidence for the existence of photons was provided in 1916 by Millikan. His results completely verified Einstein's equation and gave an accurate value for the Planck constant. The question which follows develops the ideas involved.

Q 6.10 Development question*

A photocell, figure 6.7a, is connected to a sensitive detector and the current is measured for positive and negative values of anode potential relative to the cathode. A graph of photoelectric current I against the p.d. V between the anode and cathode is shown in figure 6.7b.

(a) Explain why the current decreases as the anode potential is made more and more negative with respect to the cathode.

(b) Justify the expression

$$\tfrac{1}{2}m_e v_{max}^2 = eV_s$$

where V_s is the potential that has to be applied to stop the fastest electrons reaching the anode (called the **stopping potential**). ■

Note. From this expression the maximum speed of the photoelectrons can be determined.

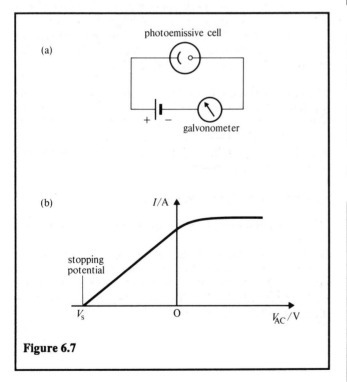

Figure 6.7

(c) If the intensity of the monochromatic light is increased from I_1 to I_2, which of the graphs, figure 6.8a or b, gives the correct relationship between photoelectric current and potential? Give a reason for your answer.

(d) If the frequency of the radiation is increased, would you expect the stopping potential to increase or decrease? Give a reason for your answer.

(e) Show that Einstein's equation can be rewritten as

$$V_s = \frac{hf}{e} - \frac{\phi}{e}$$

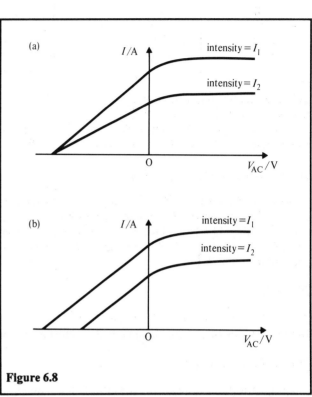

Figure 6.8

(f) In an experiment, the stopping potential was found for monochromatic light of different frequencies. A graph of V_s against f was plotted and found to be a straight line (figure 6.9).

(i) How does this fact verify Einstein's relation?
(ii) How can you obtain from the graph a value for the Planck constant h and the work function ϕ of the metal.

(Assume a knowledge of the charge of an electron.) ■

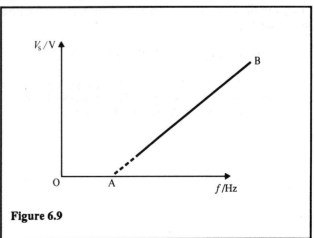

Figure 6.9

Q 6.11 Self-assessment question

The results of an experiment like Millikan's using a photocathode are as in the following table.

V_s/V	f/10^{14} Hz
0.45	5.49
1.02	6.91
1.20	7.41
1.58	8.23
2.12	9.61
3.02	11.83

(a) Plot a suitable graph and hence determine a value for h. (Charge of electron $e = -1.6 \times 10^{-19}$ C)
(b) Use your graph to determine the threshold frequency for sodium and find the work function of sodium. ∎

Q 6.12 Self-assessment question

Light of wavelength 5.9×10^{-7} m from a sodium lamp falls on a photocell and causes the emission of photoelectrons for which the stopping potential is 0.50 V. With ultraviolet of wavelength 4.0×10^{-7} m from a mercury vapour lamp, the stopping potential is 1.5 V.

Calculate

(a) a value for the Planck constant h, and
(b) the work function of the photo-cathode; state the unit. ∎

Q 6.13 Study question

Make notes on the experiment to verify Einstein's photoelectric equation and show how a value for the Planck constant can be determined from the experimental results. ∎

6.4 Wave-particle duality

The photoelectric effect can only be accounted for if the incident radiation is assumed to have particle-like properties. This picture of radiation consisting of packets of energy (quanta or photons) is also fundamental to the interpretation of optical and X-ray spectra (see topic 7). On the other hand, such phenomena as interference and diffraction are explained by assuming that light is a wave motion. Thus, a dual picture of light begins to emerge - light appears to be both a wave and a particle.

In the early twenties, Sir William Bragg remarked,

> 'On Mondays, Wednesdays and Fridays, light behaves like waves, on Tuesdays, Thursdays and Saturdays like particles, and like nothing at all on Sundays!'

This situation which, at first sight, appears to be nonsense is, in part, due to our preconceived ideas of what particles and waves should be like. The word **wave** suggests ripples on a pond, **particle** suggests things like billiard balls or bullets whose motion can be predicted by the laws of classical mechanics. The reason for the difficulty is that we are trying to relate our models to a phenomenon that can only be observed by the effects that it produces - we cannot see light. We need both the wave and particle pictures to describe the behaviour of light.

To help us understand the link between these quantum and wave pictures of light, let us consider Young's double slit experiment on the interference of light. Using modern equipment, it is possible to carry out the experiment so as to show both the wave-like and particle-like properties of light and draw some conclusions about their relationship. A detector is drawn across the pattern of dark and bright bands. The detector is a photomultiplier - a device in which the photoelectric emission of an electron results in the formation of about a million additional electrons. This constitutes a pulse of electric current which can be amplified and arranged to produce an audible 'click' when it passes through a loudspeaker. At a dark band, only a few clicks are heard as it moves through. At a bright band, the clicks rise to a maximum and then subside. Here we are detecting the arrival of photons at the screen and the pattern of bands which is a result of the action of waves.

These observations have been explained by considering that the *energy* of the light is carried by photons and their flight is *guided* by waves. They come together in those places where the wave concept implies a bright band and avoid places where the light is dim. More precisely, we can regard the *intensity* of the light at a given place as a measure of the *probability* of the photon appearing there.

The wave and particle models are complementary to one another. We require both to give a full picture of the behaviour of light. While it is travelling, we study the behaviour of the wave. When we are concerned with the emission and absorption of light, we consider the behaviour of the particle, the photon.

Q 6.14 Study/Discussion question

(a) Write a summary of the duality paradox, in your own words.
(b) There are many examples of apparent contradictions or paradoxes in physics. For example, we see ourselves on the other side of a mirror whilst knowing there is nothing there. Can you think of others? Is it harder to convince yourself and others, when the explanation is paradoxical? ∎

EXPERIMENT EN 13
Investigation with a simple photoelectric cell

Apparatus

○ electrometer, with 10^{11} Ω input resistor
○ milliammeter, 0-1 mA
○ 4 U2 cells and cell holder
○ ultraviolet lamp
○ magnesium ribbon, 100 mm length
○ glass plate
○ wire gauze

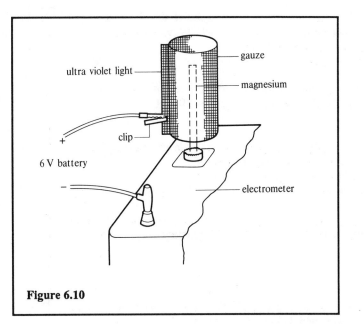

Figure 6.10

Procedure

1 Set up the apparatus as shown in figure 6.10.

2 Adjust the position of the ultraviolet lamp so that it is about 1.5 cm from the ribbon. Record the reading on the meter. What current does this represent?

3 Place a sheet of glass in front of the lamp and observe what happens.

4 What is the purpose of applying a small p.d. between the ribbon and the gauze?

5 What kind of radiation causes a current? Give a reason for your answer.

Questions on objectives

1 Which of the following is the unit of the Planck constant *h*?

A N s   D J s
B V s   E J s⁻¹
C V s⁻¹   *(objective 5)*

2 Electrons are emitted when some metal surfaces are irradiated with radiation of certain frequency ranges.
(a) What is the effect called?
(b) How has this been explained?   *(objectives 2 and 7)*

3 Explain the meaning of the statement; the threshold frequency of a certain photocell is 6.0 x 10¹⁴ Hz.
                                 (objective 1)

4 Calculate the energy of the quantum in joules associated with light of wavelength 6 x 10⁻⁷ m.
(the Planck constant = 6.6 x 10⁻³⁴ J s
speed of light = 3.0 x 10⁸ m s⁻¹)   *(objectives 5 and 10)*

5 The Einstein relation for the emission of photoelectrons from a metal due to radiation of frequency *f* can be expressed as

$$hf = \tfrac{1}{2}m_e v_{max}^2 + \phi$$

where m_e is the mass of the electron, v_{max} is the maximum speed with which it can leave the metal and ϕ is a constant for the metal called the work function.
(a) Explain what is meant by the quantity ϕ.
(b) Explain why the photoelectrons have a range of emission speeds up to a maximum value.
(c) Explain why no photoelectrons are emitted below a certain frequency of incident radiation.
                                 (objectives 6 and 8)

6 What difficulties are experienced when an attempt is made to explain the photoelectric effect by the wave theory of electromagnetic radiation?   *(objective 7)*

7 The result of an experiment to determine the work function of a metal by a photoelectric method is represented by figure 6.11.
(a) Explain what is meant by the term stopping potential V_s.
(b) Show that the work function ϕ of the metal can be obtained from the following expression

$$\phi = f_0 \times \text{gradient of graph} \times e \qquad \textit{(objective 9)}$$

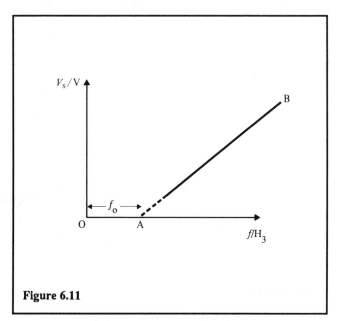

Figure 6.11

Electrons and quanta

Summary

This topic draws together threads of the previous topics to introduce the contemporary model of the atom, where electrons are located in wave patterns around the nucleus. You will study the evidence to support Bohr's quantum modification of the Rutherford model and briefly consider the limitations of Bohr's model.

The photograph shows a radiographer positioning a patient in front of an X-ray film cassette for a chest X-ray examination.

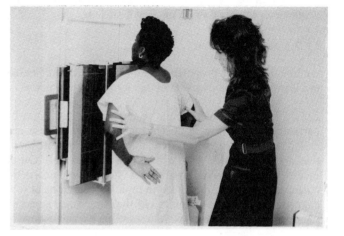

Objectives

When you have completed the work in this chapter you should be able to:

1 Use the following words and phrases with their correct scientific meaning: ionisation, ionisation potential, excitation potential, line spectra, energy, energy levels, X-ray, soft radiation, hard radiation, wave-particle duality.

2 Describe the Bohr-Rutherford model of the atom and show how it has been developed to explain the origin of line spectra.

3 Describe an experiment that confirms the existence of energy levels within the atom.

4
> **EXTENSION**
> Describe the structure of a modern X-ray tube and explain how the X-rays are produced.

5 Describe and explain the characteristics of X-ray spectra and the significance of the short wave limit.

6 Solve problems on the energy changes involved in the production of atomic spectra and X-rays.

7 Describe the spectral series of the hydrogen atom, explaining how the series are produced.

Experiments

EN 14 Ionisation by electron collision (optional) (1 hour)
EN 15 Excitation by electron collision (optional) (1 hour)

References

Akrill   Chapter 18
Caro   Chapters 4, 7, 8 and 9
Duncan   Chapter 22
Muncaster   Chapters 48 and 49
Nelkon   Chapter 34
Wenham   Chapters 43, 44 and 45
Whelan   Chapter 63

7.1 The Bohr model of the atom

Although Rutherford's model of the atom led to an understanding of the nucleus, there are problems about the behaviour of the orbiting electrons. These are accelerating and, according to classical electromagnetic theory, they must be emitting electromagnetic radiation continuously, losing energy and spiralling into the nucleus.

In 1913, in order to resolve this paradox, Bohr made use of the quantum theory to propose limitations on the energy that an electron can have when circling a nucleus.

Q 7.1 Study question

Outline Bohr's two propositions involving the ideas of stable or allowed orbit, and quanta of energy between orbits. ■

Bohr's proposals enabled him to explain the emission of particular energies from heated hydrogen gas. These are called **emission spectra** and with the corresponding **absorption spectra** provide evidence for the Bohr model. Other evidence comes from bombarding atoms with energetic particles in the way described in topic 5. Electrons at low energies can be used to interact with the electrons of atoms of a gas, and a study is made of the resulting energy changes.

Despite its successes in explaining the energy levels observed for the simplest atom, hydrogen, Bohr's theory was found to be inadequate for more complicated ones. In particular, the idea of a precise orbit for a particulate electron has had to be modified.

The ideas of wave mechanics in the last section require us to think of the electron as a wave in a pattern around the nucleus. This is called the electron **orbital**.

Background reference
Niels Bohr at 100: his life and work. This is a readable article about the man and his important work, in Physics Education, July 1986.

7.2 Evidence for energy levels

Collisions of electrons with atoms

Direct evidence of Bohr's concept of energy levels was provided by the experiment of Franck and Hertz in 1914, in which electrons collided with atoms of a gas was held at low pressure.

When this occurs, three interactions are possible:

(a) **elastic** collisions in which the bombarding electron loses a small and varying amount of kinetic energy;
(b) **inelastic** collisions in which the electrons of the gas atom gain exactly the same amounts of energy. This is called **excitation**.
(c) **inelastic** collisions in which the electrons of the gas atom gain enough energy to escape. This **ionisation** takes a certain minimum amount of energy.

E Experiment EN 14 (optional)
Ionisation by electron collision

In this experiment you will observe what happens to the conductivity of a gas as the electrons passing through it are given increasing energies.

Figure 7.1 shows a typical graph of the results obtained from the experiment EN 14. At a fairly well-defined potential (ionisation potential) the current starts to rise sharply.

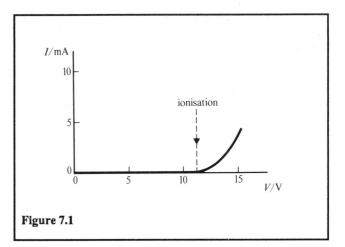

Figure 7.1

Q 7.2 Self-assessment question

(a) What does the fact that different gases have different ionisation potentials tell you?
(b) For molecular oxygen, the ionisation potential is 13.6 V. Calculate the energy necessary to remove an electron from an oxygen molecule. ■

E Experiment EN 15 (optional)
Excitation by electron collision

In this experiment you will study how the electron current through a gas-filled tube depends on the energy of the thermoelectrons and the kind of collisions between these electrons and the gas atoms.

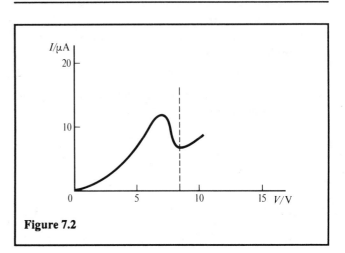

Figure 7.2

The graph (figure 7.2) shows the results obtained in experiment EN 15 using a xenon thyratron.

Refer to this graph and the experiment to answer the following questions.

Q 7.3 Development question*

(a) Which applied p.d., 6 V, 7 V, or 8.4 V resulted in (i) most electrons reaching the anode, (ii) least electrons reaching the anode?

(b) Why do more electrons reach the anode with 7 V applied than with 6 V?

(c) Suggest a reason why most electrons accelerated through 8.4 V do not reach the anode.

(d) Suggest why electrons accelerated through 7 V do not give up their energy to the gas. ■

Thus, it seems that electrons with energy of about 8 eV undergo inelastic collisions with xenon atoms and give up their energy. The xenon atoms are not ionised by this amount of energy but are able to accept this amount. Also, it seems that only that size of lump is acceptable.

We know from experiment EN 14 that xenon is ionised by energy lumps of 12.1 eV and we now have evidence that the xenon atom can accept an 'energy lump' of 8.4 eV. The absorption of this energy puts the atom in an 'energised' or excited state and we shall see later that 'excited' atoms can emit radiation when they give up their excitation energy. Experiments show that 8.4 eV is only one of several lumps of energy which will excite the xenon atom. Excitation energies are also expressed in attojoules (1 aJ = 10^{-18} J). 8.4 eV (1.3 aJ) is one of the excitation energies of xenon. 8.4 V is called an excitation potential of xenon.

Q 7.4 Study question

Write a brief summary of how the results of these experiments support Bohr's model of energy levels. ■

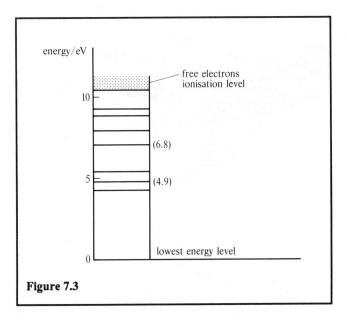

Figure 7.3

These experiments confirm that the atom can only change its energy by a number of definite amounts. These energy changes result from changes in the energy of the electrons within the atom and the results can be interpreted by thinking of the electron as moving up and down an energy ladder. If you climb a ladder, the position of the rungs determines all the possible heights at which you can stand.

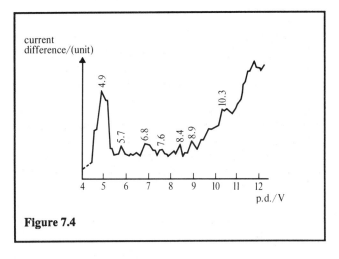

Figure 7.4

An electron energy ladder indicates all the possible electron energy levels. Of course, the rungs on this ladder are not equally spaced but all atoms of the same element have the same ladder though the ladder is very different for different elements.

Figure 7.3 shows the electron energy ladder for mercury constructed using data provided by figure 7.4 - the results of an experiment measuring the critical potentials of mercury vapour. Experiments like this cannot tell us what energy the electron has in its lowest energy state or in any excited state. But they do indicate differences in energy levels. For example, the results shown in figure 7.4 tell us that an electron in a mercury atom can receive a lump of energy of 4.9 eV or 6.8 eV but not 5.0 eV or 5.5 eV.

Q 7.5 Self-assessment question

(a) Use figure 7.3 to suggest what change in the energy state of an electron occurs when a mercury atom receives a lump of energy of (i) 10.3 eV, and (ii) 4.9 eV.

(b) If an atom of mercury vapour in the ground state has a collision with an electron of energy (i) 5.0 eV, and (ii) 10.0 eV, suggest what energy the electron might have after a collision in each case. ■

Atomic spectra

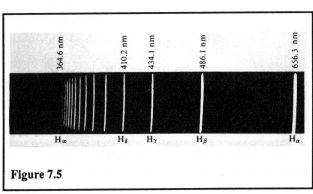

Figure 7.5

When a substance such as hydrogen is heated it is observed

to emit a spectrum which consists of electromagnetic radiation of specific wavelength. These **lines** (figure 7.5) were first discovered by Balmer, a Swiss schoolteacher. This **Balmer series** was supplemented by the discovery of similar series in the ultraviolet (**Lyman series**) and infra-red (**Paschen series**) regions.

Bohr made detailed predictions of the frequencies of the lines in the hydrogen spectrum and obtained impressive agreement with experimental results to within 1 part in 40 000 - clear evidence of the fundamental correctness of his ideas.

Bohr's theory was able to explain how the Lyman series of ultraviolet emissions is produced by electrons moving from an energy level to the ground state (see figure 7.6). The Balmer and Paschen series correspond to electrons returning from higher energy states to the -5.4 x 10⁻¹⁹ J and -2.4 x 10⁻¹⁹ J energy levels.

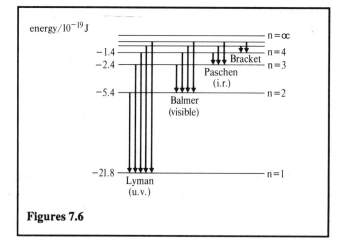

Figures 7.6

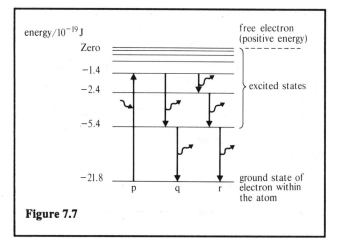

Figure 7.7

Figure 7.7 indicates the energy levels for atomic hydrogen. If we take the energy of an electron at rest outside the atom as zero then all the permitted electron energies associated with 'allowed orbits' will be negative.

The most stable state of an atom is that in which every one of its electrons is in the lowest available energy state. The hydrogen atom is most stable when its one electron is in the ground state - if the electron in the hydrogen atom is in the ground state it would need to be given 21.8 x 10⁻¹⁹ J of energy to become a free electron.

An atom is in an excited state when any of its electrons is in an allowed energy level higher than an unoccupied energy level because there is then the possibility of a return of the electron to the lower energy level with the emission of radiation.

Q 7.6 Self-assessment question

Figure 7.7 gives the allowed electron energy levels within a hydrogen atom.

(a) Calculate the frequency of the quantum of radiation which must be absorbed to raise an electron from the ground state to an energy of -1.4 x 10⁻¹⁹ J (jump 'p').
(b) Calculate the frequencies emitted if the electron returns via (i) the jumps shown as 'q', (ii) the jumps shown as 'r'.
(c) Describe what an observer would see as a result of the energy changes occurring in the jumps 'q' and 'r'. What other routes back to the ground state are there for an electron in the -1.4 x 10⁻¹⁹ J level?

7.3 X-rays

In 1895 Wilhelm Röntgen, working at Würzburg, discovered that a very penetrating radiation was being emitted from a cathode ray tube across which a high p.d. was applied. The radiation, which he named X-rays, produced fluorescence and fogging of wrapped photographic plates several metres away from the tube. Within six months, X-rays were being used for medical purposes at a hospital in Vienna and this must rate as the fastest jump from pure research to applied technology of any scientific discovery. Figure 7.8 is one of the earliest X-ray photographs made in the USA. The hand shown was hit by a shot gun blast.

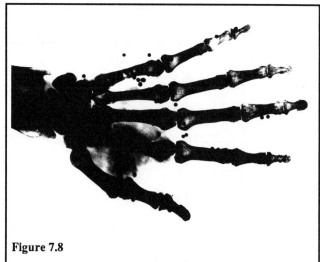

Figure 7.8

X-rays are produced when high-speed electrons strike matter and are brought to rest. To produce a strong localised source of X-rays, the electron beam must be focused on to a small spot on a target of high melting point material. The efficiency of the X-ray production is increased by using a target with a high nucleon number (tungsten is used which has a high m.p. and high nucleon number) but even then only about 0.2% of the electron beam energy is converted into X-rays.

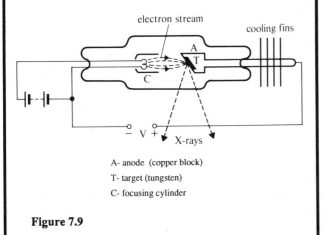
Properties of X-rays

Röntgen's discovery of X-rays was due to their ability to penetrate matter and to cause certain materials to fluoresce. Further investigation has shown that X-rays can ionise gases. X-rays travel in straight lines; they can, but with difficulty, be reflected and refracted; they can be diffracted by finely ruled gratings or regularly spaced layers of atoms in a crystal and travel at the speed of light. They are not, however, deflected by magnetic and electric fields. They can, on striking a surface, cause electrons to be ejected and the bombardment of a material by X-rays (primary) may cause the emission of a new type of X-ray (secondary).

Q 7.8 Study question

Outline the evidence in support of the belief that X-rays are electromagnetic radiation in the wavelength range 10^{-8} m to 10^{-12} m. (*Hint.* First argue that they are waves, then e.m. waves, then short e.m. waves.) ■

Q 7.9 Self-assessment question

A high intensity of X-rays was emitted from the screens of very early television sets (approaching danger level in some cases!).
(a) Why was this?
(b) How has this hazard been reduced in modern TV sets? ■

Q 7.10 Self-assessment question

(a) Which of the properties of X-rays can be used in their detection?

(b) How could you use an X-ray photograph to measure X-ray intensity? ■

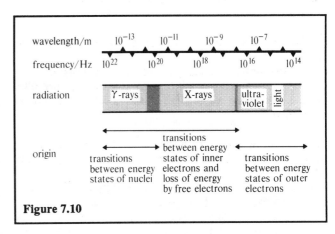

Figure 7.10

Q 7.11 Self-assessment question

(a) Use data provided in figure 7.10 to decide whether oxygen molecules can be ionised by ultraviolet radiation.
(b) Estimate how many molecules of oxygen could be ionised by a photon of X-radiation of wavelength 9.1 x 10^{-10} m.
(Ionisation energy of oxygen molecule = 22 x 10^{-19} J) ■

Application of X-rays

X-rays have important applications in the following areas:

1 **X-ray crystallography** - the analysis of structure by diffraction of X-rays (see unit *Behaviour of materials*).

2 **Radiotherapy** - the destruction of cancer cells.

3 **Radiography** - medical and industrial; an application based on the relative absorption of X-rays by different materials.

When X-rays pass through matter they lose their energy by interacting with electrons (producing photo-ionisation and electron scattering) and, therefore, the amount of absorption in a material is proportional to the electron density in the absorber. Absorption is greatest for substances with a high nucleon number (dense material). Radiography is made possible by this relative absorption in bone and tissue, etc.

The medical uses of X-rays are covered in detail in the study guide on *Medical physics* in the *Student's resource book*.

X-ray spectra

The quantum theory predicts that X-radiation of frequency f should be emitted as a packet of energy hf. The electrons in an X-ray tube are all accelerated through the same p.d. V and should reach the target with practically the same kinetic energy eV. If all this kinetic energy of a bombarding electron is converted into a *single* X-ray photon as a result of an interaction with *one* atom of the target, this results in the emission of the most energetic photon with the highest possible frequency of radiation f_{max}, where

$$eV = hf_{max}$$

Q 7.12 Self-assessmesnt question

The accelerating p.d. in an X-ray tube is 2.5×10^4 V. Calculate

(a) the kinetic energy of an electron when it reaches the target,
(b) the maximum frequency f_{max} of an emitted photon,
(c) the minimum wavelength λ_{min} emitted by the X-ray tube,
(d) the minimum wavelength if the accelerating p.d. is doubled. ∎

The **minimum wavelength** (maximum frequency) emitted by an X-ray tube is thus determined by the p.d. across the tube.
The values of λ_{min} predicted by the quantum theory are in good agreement with the experimental curves (figure 7.11) obtained by measuring the wavelength distribution of X-ray intensity at different accelerating p.d.s. In fact, measuring λ_{min} by X-ray spectrometry provides the most accurate method available for measuring the Planck constant h.

The longer wavelengths present in the **continuous spectrum** of X-radiation are due to a more gradual loss of energy by the electron which occurs when the electron shares its energy with several interacting atoms. All or part of the kinetic energy of the electron is converted into one or more photons, the rest being changed into internal energy. All target elements emit this continuous X-ray spectrum.

The third important feature of X-ray spectra is the existence of intense *lines* (K, K_β, etc.) which are characteristic of the target material. The energy produced by the bombarding electron can excite an atom by raising an electron which is very close to the nucleus into a higher energy state. X-rays of a particular frequency are emitted when this electron returns to its ground state. Just as visible line spectra provide information about the energy levels of the outermost electrons, so the X-ray line spectra provide evidence about the energy levels of the innermost electrons in the atom.

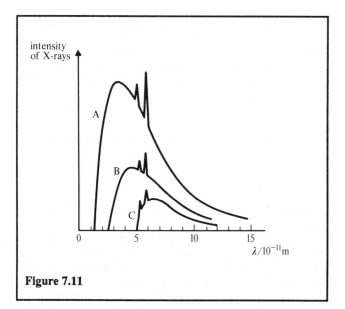

intensity of X-rays

A

B

C

0   5   10   15

$\lambda/10^{-11}$ m

Figure 7.11

Q 7.13 Self-assessment question

(a) The three spectral curves A, B and C in figure 7.11 were all obtained using the same X-ray tube.

What evidence do the curves provide to support this statement?
(b) Curve C was obtained with a p.d. across the tube of 25 kV. What were the applied p.d.s across the tube when curves A and B were obtained?
(c) Estimate a value for the Planck constant from the graph. ∎

Q 7.14 Self-assessment question

(a) More penetrating X-rays are described as 'hard' X-rays. Explain the connection between the hardness and the wavelength of the X-radiation.
(b) How can the 'hardness' of X-rays be controlled?

7.4 Electrons as waves

The wave-particle duality idea (see section 6.4) was applied to electrons by Louis Victor de Broglie in a paper which astonished physicists at the time (1927). He suggested that

> 'it is necessary to introduce the particle concept and the waves concept at the same time. The existence of particles accompanied by waves has to be assumed in all cases.'

This description of an electron as a wave can be taken as a way of expressing our uncertainty about the path followed by an individual electron. There is, in fact, no possible way of finding the exact position of an electron. Any experiment to locate the electron in 'orbit' around the nucleus would rely on getting a message about the electron's position via another probing electron or photon which interacted with it. This would inevitably change the electron orbit or remove it completely from the atom. All we can state is the probability of an electron following a particular path. The intensity of the electron wave at any point is a measure of the probability of finding an electron there. So we avoid using the word 'orbit' and refer to 'orbitals' to describe the stable electron waves pattern around a nucleus. The electron is thus not a particle located at a point but its mass and charge are 'smeared out' over the orbital in proportion to the intensity of the electron wave at each point.

By combining Planck's quantum equation $E = hf$ with Einstein's mass-energy equivalence $E = mc^2$, de Broglie derived the equation for the wavelength λ associated with mass m travelling at speed v as

$$\lambda = h/mv \quad \text{or} \quad \lambda = h/p \text{ where } p \text{ is momentum}$$

Q 7.15 Self-assessment question

Estimate the momentum of a tennis ball in ordinary play, and calculate the wavelength of the accompanying wave. ∎

Q 7.16 Self-assessment question

(a) Obtain an expression for the momentum of an electron which has been accelerated through a p.d. V.
(b) Calculate the momentum of an electron which has been accelerated through a p.d. of 5000 V.
(c) Hence use de Broglie's equation to determine the wavelength of electrons with this energy.

$$(h = 6.6 \times 10^{-34} \text{ J s}, m_e = 9.1 \times 10^{-31} \text{ kg}). ∎$$

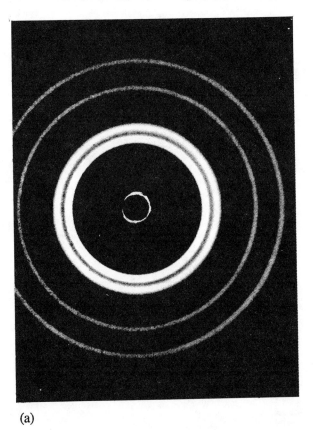

(a)

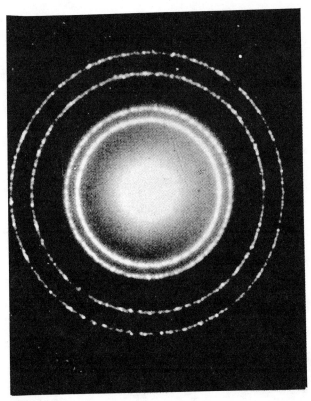

(b)

Figure 7.12

The wavelength of these electrons is of the same order of magnitude as for X-rays but, of course, the waves are very different. X-rays are electromagnetic waves, electron waves are not; X-rays are very penetrating waves while electron beams are absorbed by very thin layers of matter. However, the physical reality of an electron wave can be confirmed by diffracting electrons at a thin foil. Figure 7.12 shows a pair of diffraction patterns formed by the same aluminium foil; (a) is produced by diffraction of X-rays, (b) by diffraction of electrons of the same wavelength.

How does this wave model explain the existence of electron energy levels in the atom?

The wave mechanics model postulated that if an electron exists in a stable energy state it can be represented by a standing wave. An electron within the atom can be treated as a three-dimensional wave which is reflected by the boundaries of the atom to produce a stationary wave. Like the stationary waves set up on a guitar string such standing electron waves can have different modes of vibration. Each mode has a particular wavelength which has a particular energy level associated with it.

Thus, the emission or absorption of energy is linked to changes in the mode of vibration of an electron wave. Since each mode or vibration must contain an integral number of half-wavelengths, then only certain standing quantum waves can exist, i.e. electrons can only have certain energies.

The wave mechanics theory which evolved from the work of Schrödinger, Heisenberg, Born, etc. provides an explanation of energy changes within the atom which has been applied to such diverse and important fields as microelectronics, molecular biology and cosmology. It is, however, very mathematical and no easy physical model, such as we provided for the Rutherford and Bohr theories. For this reason, it is beyond the scope of the A-level syllabus.

Q 7.17 Study question

Why is the size of a hydrogen atom of the order of 10^{-10} m?

This is one of the questions answered by wave mechanics; a brief account can be found in Wenham, Section 45.2. ∎

Ionisation by electron collision

Apparatus

○ thyratron EN 91   884
          (xenon) (argon)
○ voltmeter 0-25 V   0-25 V
○ ammeter   0-10 mA 0-10 mA
○ resistor 1 kΩ   100 kΩ
○ thyratron base and connecting wires
○ smoothed d.c. supply 0-25 V (continuously variable)
○ 6.3 V heater supply

Note. The resistor must have a suitable power rating, e.g.
1 W or 5 W for the argon tube. Do not use a resistance box
for this purpose.

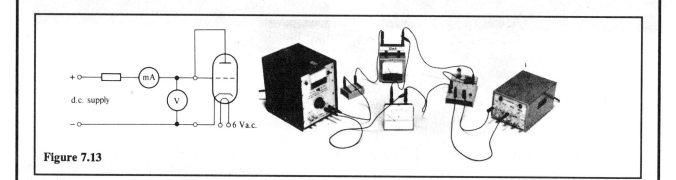

Figure 7.13

Procedure

1 Select one of the thyratrons and fit it into the appropriate holder in the base. Only one valve should be inserted into the base at a time. Connect up the circuit as shown in figure 7.13 using the appropriate resistor and meters (see apparatus list).

2 Apply a series of p.d.s between anode and cathode over the range specified. First do a trial run to ensure that the meters are appropriate and then measure and record the corresponding currents and potential difference.

3 Plot a graph of current *I* against potential difference *V* between anode and cathode.

4 Repeat the readings for the other gas and plot the *I - V* curve.

Questions

1 Why is there a current across the tube even for low p.d.s?

2 Suggest a reason why the current suddenly increases for potential differences above a certain value. (Remember that current is rate of charge flow and current increase is due to a speeding up of charge carriers or more charge carriers moving between anode and cathode.)

3 What is the anode potential at which the current starts to rise rapidly?

4 What is the energy acquired by an electron when the anode potential is the value given in question 3? The gas starts to conduct because this energy is enough to ionise a gas atom. Electrons with this energy collide with the gas atoms and give up their kinetic energy to produce ionisation. This new source of ions increases the current.

5 What is the ionisation potential of each gas?

6 What do you notice about the tube when the current starts to rise?

Excitation by electron collision

Apparatus

○ xenon thyratron, EN 91 and base
○ smoothed d.c. supply, 0-25 V variable
○ voltmeter, 0-15 V
○ galvanometer (internal light beam) or
○ microammeter, 0-100 μA
○ resistor, 10 Ω

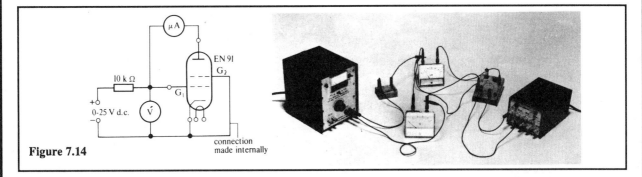

Figure 7.14

Procedure

Connect the circuit, as shown in figure 7.14. Observe and record the readings of the anode current for a range of values of the p.d. between grid G_1 and cathode. Plot a graph of current against p.d.

Interpreting the results

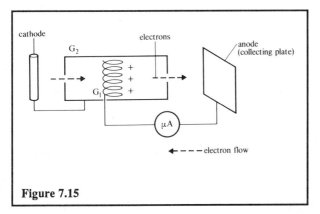

Figure 7.15

In this experiment the galvanometer detects the electrons which have enough energy to pass beyond the accelerating grid (G_1) and reach the anode. Figure 7.15 shows the arrangement of electrodes inside the thyratron. Electrons are emitted by the cathode and are accelerated through the box (G_2) by the positive potential on grid G_1 but some

will pass through G_1 and travel through the slit to be collected by the anode. The flow of electrons from the anode through the galvanometer back to G_1 keeps the anode slightly negative with respect to G_1, and the electrons travel 'up hill' from G_1 to the anode.

Figure 7.16 represents a potential hill analogue for the tube and shows the regions where electrons are accelerated, travel at constant speed, or are slowed down.

The number of electrons reaching the plate in unit time will depend on the energy they gain in moving 'downhill' and whether they lose any energy by colliding with gas atoms on the way.

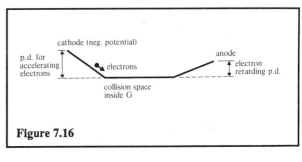

Figure 7.16

continued

EXPERIMENT EN 15

Questions

1 What happens to the kinetic energy of the electrons between cathode and grid G_1.

2 Why does the current in the tube increase initially as the grid potential is raised?

3 Suggest why the current decreases beyond a certain potential.

4 What potential difference between cathode and grid G_1 produces a minimum current in the anode circuit?

Compare your results with the graph (figure 7.2) and your answer to question 7.3 in the text.

Questions on objectives

1 Each of the following terms is related to electrons within the atom. Write a sentence which explains the meaning of each term in this context.

(a) excitation potential   (c) energy levels
(b) ionisation potential   (d) line spectra

(objective 1)

2 Outline a theory to explain the origin of line spectra. Give an equation for the frequency of one particular radiation.

(objective 2)

3 The quantum energy of a photon of yellow light from a sodium lamp is about 3.5×10^{-19} J. Which of the following would have an energy of about 7.0×10^{-19} J?

A a photon of yellow light from a source twice as bright.
B a photon, made up of two yellow radiations of nearly the same wavelength travelling together.
C a photon of ultraviolet light.
D a photon of red light.
E a photon for which the Planck constant is twice as great.

(objective 6)

4 Describe how you could show experimentally that energy levels exist within the atom. *(objective 3)*

5 Explain why several spectral lines may be grouped into a series, e.g. the Balmer series of the hydrogen spectrum.

Explain why there are three distinct series in the hydrogen spectrum, in the infra-red, visible and ultraviolet region.

(objective 7)

6 **EXTENSION** Outline how an X-ray tube operates - include a description of how the quality and intensity of the rays can be controlled. *(objective 4)*

7 Figure 7.17 (a) and (b) show intensity-wavelength graphs drawn to the same scale for two different X-ray sources.

(a) What are the features common to both these X-ray spectra?
(b) What causes these features? (You should discuss the way bombarding electrons interact with the atoms of the target to produce these features.)
(c) Suggest two reasons why these curves are not identical

(objective 5)

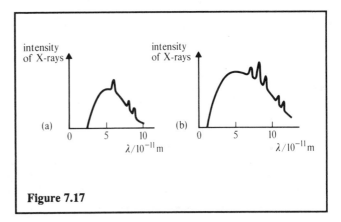

Figure 7.17

8 In an experiment to produce X-rays there is a cut-off at a wavelength of 4.8×10^{-11} m when the potential difference across the tube is 2.5×10^{4} V. Calculate

(a) the maximum energy of an X-ray photon from this tube,
(b) the maximum frequency of the X-rays, and
(c) a value for the Planck constant.

State any assumptions you have made.
($e = -1.6 \times 10^{-19}$ C, $c = 3 \times 10^{8}$ m s^{-1})   *(objective 6)*

Answers

Topic 1

1.1 (b) (i) That the device only allows an electric current to pass in one direction. (ii) The current in the circuit reaches a maximum value. This is called the saturation current.
(c) If both positive and negative charges were released by the filament then one would expect to have a current in the circuit when the anode was negative or positive relative to the filament. This is not the case.
1.3 (a) A charge of Q which is accelerated through a p.d. of V will gain energy QV. Thus, an electron which has a charge of 1.6×10^{-19} C, accelerated through a p.d. of 1 V will gain 1.6×10^{-19} C $\times$ 1 J C^{-1}, i.e. 1.6×10^{-19} J of energy. This quantity of energy is sometimes referred to as an *electronvolt* (eV) although this is not an SI unit.
(b) 4.0×10^{-19} J.
1.4 When the electron beam passes between two horizontal plates it is attracted towards the positive plate and away from the negative one. This suggests that the beam carries negative charge since unlike charges attract and like charges repel. The direction of the force which is exerted on the electron beam when it is in a magnetic field is seen to be in agreement with Fleming's left-hand rule. If the beam carries negative charge we must regard it as a current (in the conventional sense) in the opposite direction to the electron beam (figure A1).

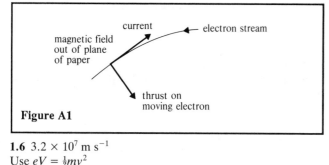

current → electron stream

magnetic field out of plane of paper

thrust on moving electron

Figure A1

1.6 3.2×10^7 m s^{-1}
Use $eV = \frac{1}{2}mv^2$
$$v = \left(\frac{2 \times 1.6 \times 10^{-19}\ \text{C} \times 3 \times 10^3\ \text{J C}^{-1}}{9.1 \times 10^{-31}\ \text{kg}}\right)$$
1.7 6.1×10^{-4} tesla
Use $\quad Bev = \dfrac{mv^2}{r}$
$$B = \frac{9.1 \times 10^{-31}\ \text{kg} \times 8.0 \times 10^6\ \text{m s}^{-1}}{1.6 \times 10^{-19}\ \text{C} \times 7.5 \times 10^{-2}\ \text{m}}$$
1.8 (a) Force exerted by the agent which establishes an electric field is here at right angles to the original direction of motion. The vertical component of the velocity continually increases in size whereas the horizontal component will remain the same (no resultant force in this direction). A mathematical analysis of the motion (which you are doing in the problem) shows that the path taken by the electrons is a parabola.
(b) 2.5×10^{-9} s
(c) 1.6×10^{-14} N upwards   use $F_E = eE$
(d) 1.8×10^{16} m s^{-2} use $F = ma$
(e) 5.6×10^{-2} m   use $s = \frac{1}{2}at^2$
(f) In a straight line which is tangential to the curve at Y.
Note. This is the principal of electrostatic deflection in a cathode ray tube, which is considered in the unit *Electronic systems*. Can you show from first principles that the path taken is a parabola and that the deflection is proportional to the p.d. between the plates?

1.9 (a) Figure A2a shows the direction of E and F_E.
(b) Figure A2b shows the direction of B and F_E.
Note. To find the direction of the magnetic field, apply Fleming's left-hand rule (electrons 'in' is the same as positive charge, i.e. current, 'out').
(c) Because the beam is undeviated, the force exerted in the electric field is equal and opposite to the force exerted in the magnetic field.
Thus $\qquad\qquad\qquad eE = Bev$
Note. This method is the basis of the velocity selector, i.e. a device used in a mass spectrometer to ensure that only particles of the same velocity enter a magnetic field. You will consider the principle of this instrument in topic 4.

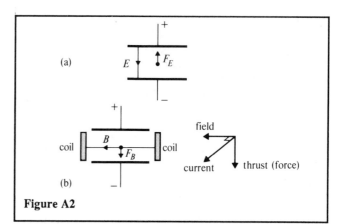

(a) E $\downarrow$ $\uparrow F_E$

coil $\quad B \quad$ coil $\qquad$ field

$\downarrow F_B$ $\qquad$ current $\qquad$ thrust (force)

(b)

Figure A2

(d) $eV = \frac{1}{2}m_e v^2$ Therefore $\dfrac{e}{m_e} = \dfrac{v^2}{2V}$
$$v^2 = \frac{E^2}{B^2} \quad \text{and} \quad E = \frac{V}{d} \quad \text{Therefore } v^2 = \frac{V^2}{B^2 d^2}$$
Substitute for v^2
Hence $\qquad\qquad\qquad e = \dfrac{V}{2B^2 d^2}$
(e) The measurements that must be made are (i) the p.d. V across the plates, (ii) the distance d between the plates, and (iii) the magnetic flux density B.
1.10 (a) The force F_B which is exerted on the electrons in the magnetic field is directed towards the centre of the circular path. The direction of the magnetic field is out of the plane of the diagram. (Direction of electron beam in absence of magnetic field is vertically upwards.)
(b) The force, Bev, exerted on the beam of electrons by the magnetic field provides the centripetal force, thus
$$Bev = \frac{m_e v^2}{r}$$
Rearranging, we have
$$\frac{e}{m_e} = \frac{v}{Br}$$
From the equation $\frac{1}{2}m_e v^2 = eV$
$$v^2 = \frac{2eV}{m_e}$$
Thus, substituting for v^2
$$\frac{e^2}{m_e^2} = \frac{2eV}{B^2 r^2 m_e}$$

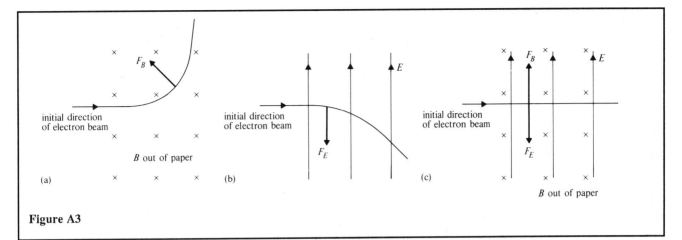

Figure A3

hence
$$\frac{e}{m_e} = \frac{2V}{B^2 r^2}$$

(c) The measurements that must be made are (i) the p.d. V between the anode and cathode of the electron gun, (ii) the radius r of the circular path, and (iii) the magnetic flux density B.

1.12 (a) 3.8×10^7 m s^{-1}

Use $eV = \frac{1}{2}m_e v^2$
$$v = \sqrt{(2 \times 1.8 \times 10^{11} \times 4000 \text{ m s}^{-1})}$$

Electron will move in a circular path of radius 0.2 m.

Use
$$Bev = \frac{mv^2}{r}$$
$$r = \frac{3.8 \times 10^7}{1.8 \times 10^{11} \times 1.0 \times 10^{-3}} \text{ m}$$

(b) 3.8×10^4 V m^{-1}

For electron to travel in its original direction
$$F_E = F_B$$
$$eE = Bev$$
Therefore
$$E = Bv$$
$$E = 1.0 \times 10^{-3} \times 3.8 \times 10^7 \text{ V m}^{-1}$$

(c) See figure A3.

1.13 (a) The Faraday constant F is the charge per mole carried by singly-charged particles (e.g. hydrogen ions) and its value can be found very precisely from electrolysis experiments.

(b) The Avogadro constant N_A is the number of specified particles per mole and, therefore, equals the number of electronic charges per mole of singly-charged particles. Its value can be found by X-ray diffraction experiments, which give the spacing of atoms in a crystal and, from this, the number of atoms per mole can be calculated.

(c) It should be clear from the above that
$$F = N_A e$$
where e is the charge carried by a singly-charged ion.

1.14 (a) (i) Earth's gravitational pull on drop, i.e. weight mg, viscous drag F which is given by the relationship
$$F = krv$$
where k is a constant, r is radius of drop, and v is the terminal velocity.
Note. $F = 6\pi\eta rv$ where η is the coefficient of viscosity.

(ii) The two forces are equal in magnitude but act in opposite directions.

(iii) This follows from (i) and (ii).

(iv) Volume of sphere $= \frac{4}{3}\pi r^3$
$$\frac{4}{3}\pi r^3 \rho g = krv_1$$

(b) (i) Weight mg (down)
Force exerted in electric field F_E (up).
$$F_E = EQ \quad \text{and} \quad E = V/d$$

(ii) When the oil drop is stationary, these two forces are equal in magnitude but act in opposite directions.
$$mg = EQ$$
Therefore
$$mg = VQ/d$$

(c) (i) Force exerted in electric field (up), weight (down), viscous drag (down). (ii) When the oil drop rises with uniform velocity, the resultant force acting on the charged drop is zero.
$$\frac{V_1 Q}{d} = mg + krv_2$$

Substitute for k from part (a)
$$k = \frac{mg}{rv_1}$$
$$\frac{V_1 Q}{d} = mg\left(1 + \frac{v_2}{v_1}\right)$$

1.16 (a) Over a period of time the mass of the water droplet will change—it will decrease because the water evaporates. The radius of the drop will decrease
$$mg = krv$$
$$\frac{4}{3}\pi r^3 \rho g = krv$$
where ρ is the density of the drop.
$$v \propto r^2$$

(b) The charge on the drop has changed.

1.17 (a)

p.d. to balance drop/V	Charge on drop $/\times 10^{-19}$ C	Multiple of N
470	4.75	3
820	3.18	2
230	6.44	4
770	1.64	1
1030	1.57	1
395	7.83	5

(b) Basic unit of charge e about 1.6×10^{-19} C

1.18 (a) 1.9×10^{-6} m

When the drop falls with uniform velocity the resultant force is zero.
$$\frac{4}{3}\pi r^3 \times 0.9 \times 10^3 \text{ kg m}^{-3} \times 9.8 \text{ N kg}^{-1}$$
$$= 6\pi \times 1.8 \times 10^{-5} \text{ N s}^{-1} \text{ m}^{-2} \times r \times 0.4 \times 10^{-3} \text{ m s}^{-1}$$
$$r^2 = \frac{6 \times 1.8 \times 10^{-5} \times 0.4 \times 10^{-3} \times 3}{4 \times 0.9 \times 10^3 \times 9.8} \text{ m}^2$$

(b) 4.8×10^{-19} C

When drop is stationary, force exerted via electric field is equal to the weight of the drop.

$$\frac{6900 \text{ J C}^{-1} \times Q}{1.3 \times 10^{-2} \text{ m}}$$
$$= \tfrac{4}{3}\pi \times (1.9 \times 10^{-6} \text{ m})^3 \times 0.9 \times 10^3 \text{ kg m}^{-3} \times 9.8 \text{ N kg}^{-1}$$
$$Q = \frac{4\pi \times 1.9^3 \times 10^{-18} \times 0.9 \times 10^3 \times 9.8 \times 1.3 \times 10^{-2}}{3 \times 6900} \text{ C}$$

Topic 2

2.4 (a) D. Alpha particles themselves cannot be seen, nor can the ions which they leave in their wake. It is the liquid condensed on those ions which is visible.
(b) The alpha particles have very little energy left at this stage, and can be deflected by the air molecules.
2.5 (a) Beta particles produce fewer ions per cm than alpha particles, which implies that β-particles are less massive than α-particles.
(b) They are easily deflected when they come close to air molecules.
2.6 Alpha particles ionise air molecules, so positive ions and electrons are produced. Electrons are attracted to the positively charged leaf, reducing its positive charge, so the leaf falls.
2.10 Beta particles. The range of alpha particles in air is less than 20 cm, so the count rate would not increase when the lead was removed. Gamma radiation (except for very 'soft' or low energy gamma radiation) will penetrate 2 mm of lead, so the count rate would not fall to background level.
2.11 Count rate $\propto \dfrac{1}{(\text{distance})^2}$

If the γ count is due to e.m. radiation (like light) the intensity will obey an inverse square law. (This is also true of other forms of radiation if there is no absorption.)
2.12 (a) Each large square represents 2.0×10^4 ion pairs. About 2.2×10^5 ion pairs produced in 70 mm track.
(b) About 4.0×10^4 fewer pairs.
(c) $2.2 \times 10^5 \times 5 \times 10^{-18}$ J is approximately 10^{-12} J.
(d) More pairs of ions are produced in a given distance because the speed of the α-particle is reduced.
2.13 (a) The intensity of radiation reaching the detector will determine the number of ions produced per second and this will determine the rate of flow of charge off the electroscope leaf.
(b) α-particles are deflected through only a small angle even by very strong magnetic fields and so a long narrow channel is required if the magnetic deflection is to prevent them from leaving.
(c) Some ionisation is produced in the electroscope perhaps by the γ-rays from the source. Even without the γ-rays from radium the leaf would slowly fall since air is not a perfect insulator.
(d) See figure A4.

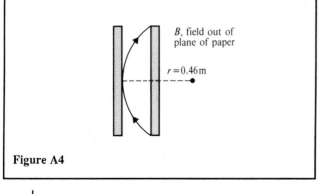

Figure A4

B, field out of plane of paper

$r = 0.46$ m

(e) $BQv = \dfrac{mv^2}{R_{\text{max}}}$, therefore $\dfrac{Q}{m} = \dfrac{v}{BR_{\text{max}}}$
(f) Connect alternate metal plates to a positive potential and the other plates to a negative potential.
(g)
$$\frac{Q}{m} = \frac{v}{R_{\text{max}}B}$$
$$\frac{Q}{m} = +5.2 \times 10^7 \text{ C kg}^{-1}$$

Q/m for α-particles is approximately half the value of Q/m for hydrogen. Later experiments by Rutherford made the ratio more exactly 1/2.
2.14 (a) Kinetic energy of α-particle
$$= \tfrac{1}{2} \times \frac{3.1 \times 10^{-19}}{5.2 \times 10^7} \times 4 \times 10^{14} \text{ J}$$
$$= 1.2 \times 10^{-12} \text{ J}$$
(b) $3.7 \times 10^{10} \text{ s}^{-1} \times 1.2 \times 10^{-12} \text{ J g}^{-1} = 4.4 \times 10^2 \text{ J g}^{-1} \text{ s}^{-1}$
(c) This is less than half the estimated power required to keep the radium 1.5 K above its surroundings ($0.12 \text{ J g}^{-1} \text{ s}^{-1}$). The rise in temperature is largely accounted for by the collision of α-particles with radium. There must be other sources of energy, e.g. β-particles, produced by the decay of the products of radium and γ emissions, not detected by Rutherford's ionisation chamber.
2.16 (a) Speed *in vacuo*.
(b) Diffraction.
(c) (i) The speed of γ and X-rays can be shown to be equal, and (ii) Crystal diffraction of γ and X-rays will show they can have a similar wavelength.
2.18 (a) Gas can escape and decay in the body cavity.
(b) Thoron gas has a very short life of less than 1 minute; α-particles cannot penetrate the bottle.

Topic 3

3.1 A mountain 10^4 m in height, which is slightly higher than Everest.
3.5 Electrostatic repulsion due to nuclear charge. The electrons produce a spherical distribution of charge and there is no field inside such a sphere (see section 2.5 of the unit *Forces and fields*).
3.6 (a) Electric potential is proportional to $1/r$.
(b) Its potential energy will increase and its kinetic energy will decrease.
3.7 See figure A5.

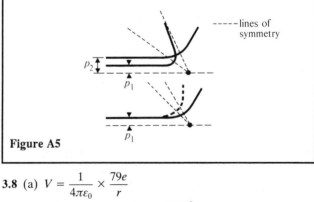

- - - - - lines of symmetry

p_2

p_1

p_1

Figure A5

3.8 (a) $V = \dfrac{1}{4\pi\varepsilon_0} \times \dfrac{79e}{r}$

(b) Potential energy $= \dfrac{1}{4\pi\varepsilon_0} \times \dfrac{158e^2}{r}$

(c) $8 \times 100^{-13\text{v}}\text{J} = 9 \times 10^9 \times 158 \times \dfrac{2.56 \times 10^{-38}}{r} \text{ J m}$
$$r = 5.0 \times 10^{-15} \text{ m}$$

3.9 Because it has half the charge and one quarter the mass it interacts less with matter.

3.10 Because they are uncharged, neutrons have very little interaction with matter.

3.12 (a) $^{19}_{9}\text{F}$ (b) 9 protons (c) 10 neutrons

3.13 Each hydrogen ion carries a charge $+e$ and so n atoms are liberated by a flow of charge of ne.

$$\frac{\text{charge flow during electrolysis}}{\text{mass of hydrogen liberated}} = \frac{ne}{nm} = \frac{e}{m}$$

where m is the mass of a hydrogen ion (a charged atom).

3.14 (a) Ions are created at different points in the tube and accelerate through different potential differences to the cathode.
(b) Slow ions.
(c) (i) Down towards the negative plate; (ii) into the plane of the diagram.

3.15 (a) To produce ionisation of the gas.
(b) Ions formed between X and Y will drift slowly towards Y and some will emerge through the slit in Y with a low velocity.
(c) Acceleration of the ions.
(d) Ions have equal energies.

ion charge × p.d. = kinetic energy

3.16 (a) $v = \dfrac{E}{B'}$

(b) 340 V;

$E = B'v = 0.20 \text{ T} \times 1.7 \times 10^5 \text{ m s}^{-1} = 3.4 \times 10^4 \text{ V m}$
$V = Ed = 3.4 \times 10^4 \text{ V m}^{-1} \times 10^{-2} \text{ m} = 340 \text{ V}$

(c) $\dfrac{Q}{m} = \dfrac{v}{Br}$

(d) The radius is proportional to the mass.

3.17 $^{35}\text{Cl} : ^{37}\text{Cl} = 3 : 1$

3.19 $^{14}_{7}\text{N} + ^{4}_{2}\text{He} \rightarrow ^{18}_{9}\text{F} \rightarrow ^{17}_{8}\text{O} + ^{1}_{1}\text{H}$

3.22 (a) $^{9}_{4}\text{Be} + ^{4}_{2}\text{He} \rightarrow ^{12}_{6}\text{C} + ^{1}_{0}\text{n}$
(b) All kinetic energy of the neutron is given to the proton.

3.23 (a) From the bottom to the top of the photograph.
(b) The lead plate slows down the particle and shows that it must be travelling from the top of the picture.
(c) The particle carries a positive charge.

3.24 (a) $^{27}_{13}\text{Al}(^{4}_{2}\alpha, ^{1}_{0}\text{n})^{30}_{15}\text{P}$
(b) A radioactive isotope of phosphorus was produced with a half-life of 3.5 minutes. (More recent experiments give 2.55 minutes.)
(c) β^+-radiation: $^{30}_{15}\text{P} \rightarrow ^{0}_{+1}\text{e} + ^{30}_{14}\text{Si}$

3.25 $^{7}_{3}\text{Li} + ^{1}_{1}\text{H} \rightarrow 2^{4}_{2}\text{He}$, α-particles were detected.

3.26 (a) Acceleration at A, constant velocity at B, negative acceleration at C.
(b) No change.
(c) Acceleration.
(d) Successive tubes are longer so that the time spent travelling between gaps by a particle will be equal and the particle can be accelerated by a constant frequency alternating p.d. The switch of the polarity of the supply is synchronised with the movement of the particle across the gaps.

(e) 500 kV.

(f) (i) Is inappropriate. The length of each tube is fixed by the frequency of the alternating supply and the velocity through that particular drift tube; (ii) and (iii) are appropriate suggestions but then the p.d. between tubes cannot be increased beyond a certain limit without producing insulation problems; (iv) is inappropriate. Final kinetic energy is not proportional to the total length. The accelerator must be extended by using more drift tubes of increasing length but you will have to persuade the government to foot the bill!

3.27 (a) It is possible if the frequency of the alternating potential difference is increased to compensate for the rate at which the particle speed increases.
(b) The magnetic field must increase. B must be proportional to v if r is to remain constant.

Topic 4

4.1 (a) 88 protons (b) 138 neutrons

4.2 (b) $^{214}_{83}\text{Bi} \xrightarrow{\alpha} ^{210}_{81}\text{Tl}$
$\downarrow \beta \qquad \downarrow \beta$
$^{214}_{84}\text{Po} \xrightarrow{\alpha} ^{210}_{82}\text{Pb} \xrightarrow{\beta} ^{210}_{83}\text{Bi}$

4.3 (a) 4 (b) 1/16 (c) 255/256

4.4 E

4.5 A

4.6 0.0133 s^{-1} $\left(\lambda = \dfrac{0.693}{52} \text{ s}^{-1} \right)$

4.7 (a) 2.66×10^{21} (b) $1.4 \times 10^{-11} \text{ s}^{-1}$ (c) $5.0 \times 10^{10} \text{ s}$

4.8 (a) Gas can escape and decay in the body cavity.
(b) Thoron gas has a half-life of less than 1 minute. α-particles cannot penetrate the bottle.

4.11 6 litres.

Topic 5

5.1 (a) For diffraction to be observable, the electron wavelength must be of the order of the nuclear diameter—this requires high momentum electrons.

(b) Diameter of nucleus $= \dfrac{1.22 \times 3 \times 10^{-15}}{\sin 43°} \text{ m}$
$\approx 5 \times 10^{-15} \text{ m}$

Volume of nucleus $= \frac{4}{3}\pi \times 2.53 \times 10^{-45} \text{ m}^3 \approx 6 \times 10^{-44} \text{ m}^3$
(c) Mass of oxygen nucleus $= 2.7 \times 10^{-26} \text{ kg}$
Density of oxygen nucleus $= 4.5 = 10^{17} \text{ kg m}^{-3}$
(d) 4.5×10^{14} denser than water

5.2 Mass of lithium-7 nucleus $= 7.0145$ u
Mass decrease of 0.0188 u (calculated using nuclear masses). The mass decrease can also be obtained using atomic masses throughout, i.e. including the masses of four electrons on each side of the following equation.
$$^{7}_{3}\text{Li} + ^{1}_{1}\text{H} \rightarrow 2^{4}_{2}\text{He}$$

5.3 $9 \times 10^{13} \text{ J}$

5.4 (a) $m = \dfrac{4.2 \times 10^5 \text{ J}}{9 \times 10^{16} \text{ m}^2 \text{ s}^{-2}} \approx 5 \times 10^{-12} \text{ kg}$

(b) Number of molecules in 1 kg of water $= \dfrac{1000}{18} \times 6 \times 10^{23}$

Energy change per molecule $= \dfrac{3 \times 4.2 \times 10^5}{1000 \times 10^{23}} \text{ J} \approx 10^{-20} \text{ J}$

5.5 (a) $\Delta m = \dfrac{\Delta E}{c^2} \dfrac{1.6 \times 10^{-13} \text{ J}}{(3.0 \times 10^8 \text{ m s}^{-1})^2} = 1.8 \times 10^{-30} \text{ kg}$

Mass equivalent of 1 MeV is $2m_\text{e}$
(b) Mass of 1 MeV β-particle = (rest mass + mass of kinetic energy)
$= 2.7 \times 10^{-30} \text{ kg}$

5.6 (a) An *increase* in mass of 0.0012 u. (The calculation can be made using the data for the mass of whole atoms and including nine electron masses on each side of the equation.)
(b) No. *More* energy must be supplied to produce a mass increase.
(c) The energy supplied by the high speed α-particle.
(d) To produce a mass increase of 0.0012 u, 1.1 MeV are required. 6.6 MeV are shared between oxygen nucleus and proton.

5.7 (a) Mass of $^2_1$H nucleus = 2.0141 u − 0.0005 u
$$= 2.0136 \text{ u}$$
$$\text{Mass of n + p} = 2.0160 \text{ u}$$
$$\text{Mass defect} = 0.0024 \text{ u}$$
(b) Mass defect of α particle = 4.0320 u − 4.0015 u
$$= 0.0305 \text{ u}$$
5.8 28 MeV (0.0305 × 930 MeV)
5.9 (a) Yes. Three points along $Z = 8$, two at $Z = 17$ and ten at $Z = 50$.
(b) $N = Z$
(c) The ratio increases.
(d) Nuclei with the largest mass.
(e) Hydrogen, helium-3.
5.10 Yes. A total binding energy of 28 MeV equals 7 MeV per nucleon.
5.11 (a)

	Nuclear mass/u	Mass defect/u	Binding energy per nucleon/MeV
^{16}O	15.9909	0.1371	7.98
^{17}O	16.9951	0.1416	7.75
^{18}O	17.9951	0.1503	7.77

(b) Yes; a peak for ^{16}O at about 8 MeV per nucleon.
(c) ^{16}O has the greatest binding energy per nucleon and is, therefore, the most stable and most abundant (99.76%). ^{17}O and ^{18}O are less stable and less abundant (^{17}O least abundant 0.04%).
5.12 (a) Z increases by one; N decreases by one; N/Z decreases (neutron excess decreases).
(b) Diagonally down and to the right.
(c) (i) β^- emitters will be located above the plot for stable nuclides so that the emission produces a move towards the line of stable nuclides. (ii) β^+ emitters will be located below the plot for stable nuclides.
5.13 $^{238}_{92}$U $\rightarrow$ $^{234}_{90}$Th + $^4_2$He
5.14 (a) $Z = 82$, $A = 208$. A stable isotope of lead.
(b) The decay series must lead to increased stability by a decrease in the ratio N/Z. This is only possible by β^- emission. α-emission alone leads to an increase in the ratio N/Z.
5.17 $^{235}_{92}$U + $^1_0$n $\rightarrow$ $^{236}_{92}$U $\rightarrow$ $^{141}_{56}$Ba + $^{92}_{36}$Kr + 3$^1_0$n
5.18 (a) One. Yes, it is just possible for a chain reaction to be established.
(b) No. On average more than two of the product neutrons will escape and the reaction will not be self-sustaining.
(c) The reproduction factor exceeds one. A chain reaction would be set up with increasing energy emission—an uncontrolled chain reaction.
(d) Critical mass is the smallest mass of a fissile material in which a chain reaction can occur. The reproduction factor is one for critical mass.

5.20 (a) To slow down neutrons.
(b) Neutron energy is given to the nuclei of the moderator.
(c) A material makes a good moderator if it has a low mass so that there is a large amount of kinetic energy transferred on the collision. It must be able to absorb these high amounts of energy without becoming unstable.
(d) Boron can capture a neutron and be transformed into a stable isotope.
(e) Pushing the control rods *in* produces more neutron capture. Pulling the rods *out* increases the reproduction factor until the pile becomes critical. Pulling out the rods too quickly could produce an uncontrolled chain reaction (reproduction factor much greater than one).

5.21 $^{238}_{92}$U + $^1_0$n $\rightarrow$ $^{239}_{92}$U
$$\swarrow$$
$$^{239}_{93}\text{Np} + ^{\ 0}_{-1}\text{e}$$
$$\searrow$$
$$^{239}_{94}\text{Pu} + ^{\ 0}_{-1}\text{e}$$
5.23 (a) 2^2_1H $\rightarrow$ $^3_2$He + $^1_0$n
(b) Mass change in fusion of 2^2_1H = 0.0035 u = 5.8 × 10^{-30} kg
$$\text{Energy release} = 5.8 \times 10^{-30} \text{ kg} \times (3 \times 10^8 \text{ m s}^{-1})^2$$
$$= 5.2 \times 10^{-13} \text{ J per fusion of 4.0 u}$$
$$(4.0 \text{ u} = 6.6 \times 10^{-27} \text{ kg})$$
$$\text{Energy release per kilogram} = \frac{5.2 \times 10^{-13} \text{ J}}{6.6 \times 10^{-27} \text{ kg}}$$
$$= 7.9 \times 10^{14} \text{ J kg}^{-1}$$
(Enough energy to keep a town of 20 000 people supplied with energy for a lifetime.)
5.24 Raise the matter to extremely high temperature.
5.25 (a) Particle X is a positron (β^+)
(b) Y is $^3_2$He
(c) Z is a proton
(d) 6^1_1p = $^4_2$He + 2^1_1p + $2^{\ 0}_{+1}$e
or 4^1_1p = $^4_2$He + $2^{\ 0}_{+1}$e

Topic 6

6.1 (a) (i) The negative charge on the zinc repels the negative charges (electrons) which are released from the surface of the zinc by the ultraviolet and hence the electroscope is discharged. (ii) When the zinc plate is positively charged the negative charges are attracted and fail to escape, hence the electroscope remains charged.
(b) The sheet of glass absorbs most of the ultraviolet light and the visible light which passes through does not cause negative charges to be emitted from the surface of the zinc.
6.2 (a) Whether the frequency is high enough.
(b) The intensity of the incident radiation.
(c) The photoelectrons are released from a surface with a range of speeds from zero up to a maximum value. The maximum speed of emission increases as the frequency of the radiation increases and is independent of the intensity of the radiation.
(d) The threshold frequency. If the frequency of the incident radiation is less than this value, no electrons are emitted even if the intensity of the radiation is very great.
6.4 (a) The red and blue light have the same amplitude and, therefore, on the basis of the wave theory the energy which is falling on unit surface once every second is the same. If the blue light has sufficient energy to enable electrons to be released, one would expect them also to be released by red light. This does not happen and, therefore, the observation is in conflict with the theory.
(b) If the surface receives more energy and only a certain amount is required to release an electron, then it is reasonable to suppose that the kinetic energy of a certain number of the emitted electrons would be increased. This does not happen—the maximum speed is independent of the intensity of the radiation.
(c) That the number of photoelectrons emitted per second is dependent upon the intensity of the radiation. If the radiation has a greater intensity, more will be absorbed by the surface and, therefore, it is possible for more electrons to escape.
Note. On the basis of the wave theory, the energy is spread over the whole of the wavefront and, therefore, the amount of the incident energy received by any one electron would be small—a time interval would be expected before a further electron had sufficient energy to escape. This does not occur

and, in fact, electrons are emitted instantaneously even if the intensity of the radiation is very low.

6.5 (a) The frequency of the blue light is greater than the frequency of red light. Thus, a 'blue photon' has more energy than a 'red photon'. The 'red photon' does not have sufficient energy to release an electron from the surface whereas the 'blue photon' does.

(b) The rate at which the electrons are emitted would increase.

(c) The energy of the 'green photon' is equal to the minimum energy that is required to extract an electron from the surface. Thus, $$hf_0 = \phi$$ where f_0 is the threshold frequency.
This particular metal has a threshold frequency in the green part of the visible spectrum.

(d) If the frequency of the radiation is higher than the threshold frequency, the extra energy is carried away as the kinetic energy of the emitted electron. The frequency of ultraviolet is greater than the frequency of blue light, therefore, an 'ultraviolet photon' has more energy than a 'blue photon'. This means more kinetic energy is given to an electron by the ultraviolet than by blue light. The electrons will thus have a higher maximum speed.

6.6 (a) hf is the energy of the incident photon. ϕ is the minimum energy required to liberate an electron from the surface of the metal. $\frac{1}{2}m_e v_{max}^2$ is the maximum kinetic energy of the emitted electron.

(b) Because some of the electrons, e.g. those relatively far below the surface, may need more than the minimum energy in order to escape from the surface.

(c) $hf_0 = \phi$
Thus $$hf - hf_0 = \frac{1}{2}m_e v_{max}^2$$

6.7 5.0×10^{-20} J
Using $hf - \phi =$ max. k.e. and $c = f\lambda$
$$E_k = 6.6 \times 10^{-34} \text{ J s} \times \frac{3.0 \times 10^8 \text{ m s}^{-1}}{5.6 \times 10^{-7} \text{ m}}$$
$$- 1.9 \text{ J C}^{-1} \times 1.6 \times 10^{-19} \text{ C}$$

6.8 $[E] = \text{M L}^2 \text{ T}^{-2}$ $[f] = \text{T}^{-1}$

6.9 (a) 2.0×10^5 Hz, 1.3×10^{-28} J, 3.0×10^{33} photons per second
(b) 5.1×10^{14} Hz, 3.4×10^{-19} J, 1.5×10^{20} photons per second

6.10 (a) The current is due to a flow of photoelectrons emitted from the photocathode. If the anode is at a negative potential, the agent that sets up the electric field exerts a force on the electrons which repels the electrons instead of attracting them. As the field is increased, more and more electrons are prevented from reaching the anode. Eventually, a potential difference will be reached at which all the electrons are prevented from arriving at the anode.

(b) eV_s is the work done on the electron when it decelerates through a stopping p.d. of V_s. This is equal to the kinetic energy $\frac{1}{2}mv^2$ of the emitted electron.

(c) Graph (a). The intensity of the light determines the number of electrons emitted per unit time and not the maximum speed of the electrons. Graph (b) implies that when the intensity is increased, the maximum speed increases because a greater stopping potential is required to prevent any current flowing. This is incorrect.

(d) Increase. The electrons leaving the surface would have a higher maximum kinetic energy and thus a higher negative potential would have to be applied to stop the current.

(e) $hf = \phi + \frac{1}{2}m_e v^2$
But $$\frac{1}{2}m_e v^2 = eV_s$$
Therefore $$hf = \phi + eV_s$$
Hence $$V_s = \frac{hf}{e} - \frac{\phi}{e}$$

(f) (i) The equation, i.e. the rewritten form of Einstein's relation, says that when the stopping potential V_s is plotted as a function of frequency f, the graph should be a straight line. The experimental results gave a straight line graph; thus, the Einstein relation was verified.

(ii) Gradient of graph $= h/e$
Therefore $h =$ gradient of graph $\times$ charge of electron
The intercept OA on the x axis is equal to the threshold frequency f_0.
When V_s is zero, $0 = \dfrac{hf_0}{e} - \dfrac{\phi}{e}$
that is $\phi = hf_0$

6.11 (a) The Planck constant $= 6.4 \times 10^{-34}$ J s
Graph of V_s against f is shown in figure A6
$$hf = \phi + eV_s$$
$$V_s = \frac{hf}{e} - \frac{\phi}{e}$$
gradient of graph $= h/e = 4.0 \times 10^{-15}$ V s
Therefore $h =$ gradient of graph $\times e$
$$h = 4.0 \times 10^{-15} \text{ J C}^{-1} \text{ s} \times 1.6 \times 10^{-19} \text{ C}$$

(b) Work function $\phi = 2.7 \times 10^{-19}$ J or 1.7 eV
When V_s is zero, frequency is threshold frequency f_0, that is $\phi = hf_0$
From graph $f_0 = 4.3 \times 10^{14}$ Hz
$$\phi = 4.3 \times 10^{14} \text{ s}^{-1} \times 4.0 \times 10^{-15} \text{ J C}^{-1} \text{ s} \times 1.6 \times 10^{-19} \text{ J}$$

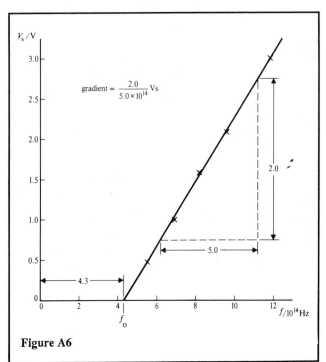

Figure A6

6.12 (a) 6.7×10^{-34} J s (b) 2.6×10^{-19} J or 1.6 eV
Use $hf = \phi + eV_s$ and $c = f\lambda$, where $c = 3 \times 10^8$ m s^{-1}, $f_v = 5.1 \times 10^{14}$ Hz and $f_{uv} = 7.5 \times 10^{14}$ Hz
$$h(5.1 \times 10^{14} \text{ Hz}) = \phi + 1.6 \times 10^{-19} \text{ C} \times 0.5 \text{ V}$$
$$h(7.5 \times 10^{14} \text{ Hz}) = \phi + 1.6 \times 10^{-19} \text{ C} \times 1.5 \text{ V}$$
Use these two equations to find a value for h.
Substitute in one of the equations for h and hence determine a value for ϕ.

Topic 7

7.2 (a) Different molecules/elements need different quantities of energy to remove an electron.

(b) Energy needed = $1.6 \times 10^{-19} \times 13.6$ J
$$= 2.2 \times 10^{-18} \text{ J}$$

7.3 (a) (i) 7 V   (ii) 8.4 V
(b) The electrons accelerated through 7 V travel faster than those accelerated through 6 V and a greater proportion overcome the retarding p.d. and reach the anode.
(c) Electrons accelerated through 8.4 V have a kinetic energy of 8.4 eV and these electrons collide inelastically with atoms and give up all their energy to ionise the atom. After collision with the gas, these electrons do not have any energy to overcome the retarding p.d. near the anode.
(d) The gas atoms cannot accept an amount of energy less than 8 eV and so electrons with energy 7 eV collide elastically and retain their kinetic energy.

7.5 (a) (i) An electron originally in the lowest level (ground state) becomes a free electron (ionisation).
(ii) An electron moves from the 4.9 eV level to the 6.8 eV level.
(b) (i) After collision it could have energy 0.1 eV or 0.3 eV since the mercury atom has excitation energies of 4.7 eV, 1.6 eV, 3.2 eV, etc.

(ii) Possibly 1.2 eV (since there is a pronounced excitation potential at 8.8 V but it could have many other energies, 1.4 eV, 1.6 eV, 3.2 eV, etc.

7.6 (a) 3.9×10^{15} Hz
$$E_1 - E_2 = hf$$
$$f = \frac{(21.8 - 1.4) \times 10^{-19}}{6.6 \times 10^{-34}} \text{ Hz}$$
(b) (i) $f_1 = 6.0 \times 10^{14}$ Hz, $f_2 = 2.5 \times 10^{15}$ Hz
(ii) $f_1 = 1.5 \times 10^{14}$ Hz, $f_2 = 4.5 \times 10^{14}$ Hz, $f_3 = 2.5 \times 10^{15}$ Hz
(c) For jumps 'q'; f_1 is a visible emission of green light ($\lambda = 5 \times 10^{-7}$ m). f_2 is ultraviolet.
For jumps 'r'; only f_2 gives visible radiation; red ($\lambda = 6.6 \times 10^{-7}$ m). f_1 is infra-red and f_3 is ultraviolet.
Other routes back are
$$(-1.4 \rightarrow -2.4 \rightarrow 21.8) \times 10^{-19} \text{ J}$$
$$\text{or } (-1.4 \rightarrow -21.8) \times 10^{-19} \text{ J}$$

7.9 (a) Electrons with high energy being stopped at screen—corresponds to an X-ray tube.
(b) Reducing the accelerating potential will reduce the penetrating power of X-rays (may need an improved phosphor as picture will become fainter). Use lead glass for screen, i.e. glass which contains lead atoms—lead is a good absorber.

7.10 (a) Early detection used fluorescence and the photographic plate. Photography still plays an important role in medicine and crystallography where it offers a permanent record of an investigation.
For obtaining an immediate and quantitative measurement, ionisation is utilised, e.g. a GM tube or an ionisation chamber.
(b) A photocell measures the intensity of light transmitted through the exposed negative film.
Limitations: the ability of the film to translate relative X-ray intensities into varying density of image; the ability of the photocell to translate varying density of image into changes in the deflection of a meter or pen recorder.

7.11 (a) Yes. A photon of energy 22×10^{-19} J has frequency 3.3×10^{15} Hz and wavelength 9.1×10^{-8} m. This is within the u.v. range.
(b) 100

7.12 (a) Kinetic energy $= eV = 4.0 \times 10^{-15}$ J
(b) $f_{max} = \dfrac{4.0 \times 10^{-15} \text{ J}}{6.6 \times 10^{-34} \text{ J s}} = 6.1 \times 10^{18}$ Hz
(c) $\lambda_{min} = 4.9 \times 10^{-11}$ m
(d) $\lambda_{min} = 2.4 \times 10^{-11}$ m

7.13 (a) The characteristic line spectra have the same wavelengths on all curves indicating that the same target was used in all cases.
(b) A, 100 kV; B, 50 kV; ($f_{max} \propto V$, $\lambda_{min} \propto 1/V$)
(c) $h = 6.7 \times 10^{-34}$ J s
$$h = \frac{eV}{f_{max}} = \frac{eV\lambda_{min}}{c}$$
$$= \frac{1.6 \times 10^{-19} \text{ C} \times 25 \times 10^3 \text{ V} \times 5 \times 10^{-11} \text{ m}}{3 \times 10^8 \text{ m s}^{-1}}$$

7.14 (a) A higher energy photon will penetrate further into matter. Harder X-rays are emitted as higher energy (higher frequency) photons. Shorter wavelength X-rays are harder.
(b) By controlling the p.d. across the tube. Increasing the accelerating p.d. will decrease the value of λ_{min} and move the X-ray energy distribution towards the shorter wavelength region producing harder X-rays.

7.16 (a) $\frac{1}{2}m_e v^2 = eV$
Therefore $m_e v = \sqrt{(2em_e v)}$
(b) $m_e v = 3.8 \times 10^{23}$ kg m s^{-1}
(c) $\lambda = \dfrac{h}{m_e v} = \dfrac{6.6 \times 10^{-34} \text{ J s}}{3.8 \times 10^{23} \text{ kg m s}^{-1}} = 1.7 \times 10^{-11}$ m

Index

References

These textbooks may be referred to at the start of each topic. Full details are to be found in the Student's resource book.

Akrill   Akrill, T.B. Bennet, G.A.G. and Miller, G.J. *Physics*.
           Edward Arnold

Caro   Caro, De. McDonell, J.A. and Spicer, B.M. *Modern physics:*
           An introduction to atomic and nuclear physics
           Edward Arnold

Duncan   Duncan,T. Physics: *A text book for advanced level students.*
           John Murray

Muncaster   Muncaster, R. *A-level Physics*
           Stanley Thorne

Nelkon   Nelkon, M and Parker, P. *Advanced Level Physics*
           Heinemann

Wenham   Wenham, E.J. and others. *Physics: Concepts and Models*
           Longman

Whelan   Whelan, P.M and Hodgson, M.J. *Essential Principles of Physics*
           John Murray

Acknowledgements

Thanks are due to the following, who have kindly permitted the reproduction of copyright photographs; Page 2, Sony International ; Figs 1.7, P13, 2.4, 2.10, 7.5, Science Museum; Fig 21, Ulistein Bilderdienst; Figs 2.3, 2.21, p29, Cavendish Laboratorys; Fig 2.9, P.Kapitza (1924) Proc. Royal Soc; P42, Popperfoto; Fig 4.6 Royal Marsden Hospital; P56, J.Allan Cash Photo Library; Fig 5.8, Open University; P67, BBC Hulton Picture Library; Fig 7.12, EDC;

The following photographs are by Martin Sookias and Martin Thornton; Figs 1.1, 1.3, 1.4, 3.14, 7.13, 7.14.

The following photographs are by Tony Langham; Cover and Figs 1.2, 2.15, 2.16, 2.17, 2.18, 2.19, 2.20, 4.9, 4.10.

Every effort has been made to contact the copyright holders of Figs, 1.2, 1.5, 1.8, 3.9, 4.7, 7.8. who kindly gave permission for reproduction in the first edition. The authors and publishers regret these omissions and will be pleased to rectify them in a future printing.

95